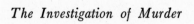

The Investigation of Murder

The Investigation of Murder

PROFESSOR FRANCIS E. CAMPS
with Richard Barber

MICHAEL JOSEPH * LONDON

First published in Great Britain by
MICHAEL JOSEPH LTD
26 Bloomsbury Street
London, W.C.1
1966

© 1966 by Francis E. Camps and Richard Barber

Set and printed in Great Britain by Tonbridge Printers Ltd,
Peach Hall Works, Tonbridge, Kent, in Baskerville eleven on
thirteen point, on paper made by Henry Bruce at Currie,
Midlothian, and bound by The Dorstel Press, Harlow

CONTENTS

ILLUSTRATIONS

(following page 72)

Introduction

The subject of crime and its detection has always exercised a peculiar fascination for those who read. And of all types of crime, murder – both in fact and fiction – easily leads the field. In the factual sphere, whereas some of the most interesting cases pass almost unnoticed, those with the sensational ingredients of sex and emotional appeal will produce a spate of publications often covering the same ground. For this reason, this book makes no attempt to give a complete record of the cases mentioned but merely provides an adequate outline to introduce the matters which we consider relevant to our arguments.

Nor is it the intention of this book to enter into discussions concerning innocence or guilt, except when the purpose for which it is written so demands, but rather to use a number of cases as a framework to illustrate the advances or otherwise which have taken place in the scientific aspects of detection.

In the first part, we propose to build up, by studying a selection of cases of special interest, a picture of the role that the scientists could play in the detection of crime. It is a truism to say that the motives of crime do not vary; but the means at the criminal's disposal have varied and increased enormously over the last half-century and it is hoped that these cases will illustrate the extent to which detection, both scientific and otherwise, has kept up with the commission of crimes, or has failed to do so. At the same time, it must be appreciated that any failure of science may be due to the shortcomings of its use and not entirely to its own weakness.

The cases chosen range from those apparently impossible

of solution, through the very difficult, to the obvious – and the latter may be the most misleading. For this no apology is offered. In the solution of the simple crime, with motive, clues and ample evidence, and a criminal who is neither a persistent offender – a so-called 'professional' – or a man who has devoted any thought to his crime, the police, with or without the aid of science, are undoubtedly more efficient and expert in the job of bringing the culprit to justice than they were fifty years ago. This is not surprising for they are now assisted by better records, organisational aids, and scientific assistance. Even here, it may be that there is still room for improvement, but the weaknesses are less obvious and need no lengthy explanation. On occasions it may be possible that the advance of science has made the investigating officer tend to lean on it too heavily rather than use his own judgment, to the detriment of the latter.

But it is disappointing to find that, where forensic science might really succeed, in the apparently motiveless or exceptionally well planned crime, it has on several occasions in recent years notably failed to do so. However, it must be accepted at the outset that, for every unsolved or unsatisfactorily solved medicolegal case, there are two where the investigation has succeeded. Certainly it is not suggested that the scientist cannot contribute to law enforcement, for this would be absurd. It is merely the object of this book to emphasise that it may be that his skills are neither sufficiently understood nor adequately deployed. Some of the cases which are included must rank among the most historically interesting; unfortunately, they are quite often both sensational and intractable to solution. As a result, they have received more attention relative to their real importance than other similar cases which have been successfully solved.

The chief charge in any indictment that follows is a single and very elementary one : that the scientists who are involved in police investigations have on occasions failed to observe the basic requirements of scientific methods and that police and lawyers without adequate scientific training have failed to realise this. On occasions, this has been asking the impossible because in some cases the evidence was no longer in its original state when examined at the scene of the incident, because of outside interference; in others lack of experience on the part of the observer has resulted in the opportunity for proper initial examination being totally inadequate. The remedy for both these faults will require new organisation of facilities and personnel which must mean the reform of existing arrangements. There are already signs that this is happening. Even more serious and much more difficult is the problem of the proper assessment of scientific evidence by the court. The implications of pseudo-science and lack of scientific knowledge, even among experts, will recur again and again in the cases and the discussion of them. Last, and almost the most dangerous of all, are the occasions when a scientist has chosen to turn advocate rather than impartial witness, a fault which is easy once he becomes emotionally involved and decides for himself whether a person is guilty or not. These incidents are the hardest to prove, but it has undoubtedly happened that scientists have known what the police have wanted them to see, and have duly seen it. It may be that a guilty man would have got away 'scot-free' if it had not been for this; but it is essential to the concept of justice as we know it that a man can only be convicted on the evidence produced and accepted in court.

An excellent example of this was seen in the trial of John Donellan in 1781 for the murder of his brother-in-law, by administering laurel water in place of his medicine. The evidence of witnesses as to symptoms of the victim's fatal illness was more than enough to show the guilt of the accused. Yet the medical witnesses chose to base their case on the argument that the appearances at autopsy eleven days after death were due to the poison and they tried to substantiate this opinion by comparing them with the appearances immediately after death in animals which they had killed with laurel water. This evidence was contradicted by the famous John Hunter, who quite rightly said that the autopsy appearances resulted from decomposition. Had the medical experts adhered to voicing an opinion based on the symptoms as described by witnesses, then their evidence would not have been open to criticism. Instead, they pursued a different and unnecessary approach which appeared to be more 'scientific'. If they had wished to use a scientific argument from the autopsy findings, they should have at least opened the skull or intestines, or attempted to perform an analysis. Perhaps ignorance might for them be held an adequate excuse; but today, when the majority of educated laymen have some concept of the implications of scientific method, similar if more subtle misuses of science still occur; and there is not always a John Hunter to expose them.

PART ONE

1 A New Look at Jack the Ripper

The settings and characters of the most famous series of all homicidal crimes take us back to the streets of London as depicted by Hogarth at his most vicious. The squalid, living hell of Gin Alley, where oblivion through alcohol was the only escape from the misery of real life, should no longer have been found in the larger London of the 1880's, soot-begrimed and grey. Yet a whiff of the old atmosphere hung over the less savoury parts of the East End still, and even among the more respectable areas there remained a few corners where drunken bodies lay huddled every night on staircases or at the foot of walls, and where women would still sell themselves for a few pence to get their next glass of gin, or somewhere to sleep for the night. The police showed no great concern for these creatures, who sometimes served to keep the sailors from too much mischief, and were content to leave them in peace, while avoiding the unsavoury corners where they chose to make their stand. An occasional violent death in this area could pass almost without comment as being the result of some drunken seamen's brawl; and in the murk of the ill-lit back alleys, where the police only ventured in pairs, robbery and assault were easy to commit without the risk of positive identification.

Of the many honest citizens of Whitechapel who had to tolerate this state of affairs, Albert Crow was only one of many late revellers on the evening of August Bank Holiday of 1888. He had been one of the crowds who had thronged the streets in festive mood and perhaps had gone to one of the many fairs, of which the most famous was that on Hampstead Heath. Londoners of those days, with poor transport facilities and less money, tended to seek their pleasures nearer to home than today; and there were more who took the day off for drinking sessions, in music halls or the pubs, which stayed open till all hours to cater for them. So, as Crow groped up the staircase at 35 George Yard Buildings at half past three in the morning, the huddled form of a woman on the stairs caused him no surprise. He let sleeping dogs lie and went up to bed.

It was only when one of his neighbours, John Reeves, who had got up early to go to look for a job, came down at 5 a.m. the following morning, that Crow's mistake was discovered. In the half-light, Reeves saw not drunkenness but death, for the form of the night before was now seen to be a corpse with 'extensive injuries' (a masterpiece of understatement!) lying in a pool of blood. He ran at once for the police who soon identified the dead woman as Martha Tabrown, otherwise Martha Turner, well known in the neighbourhood as a prostitute, and living apart from her husband. Her usual stand was nearer the Tower of London. They also discovered that another woman living in George Yard Buildings had arrived home at 2 a.m. and, when going out again at 2.10 a.m. to get some fish and chips, had seen nothing. Admittedly such women were often intoxicated, but they also have a second sight for self-protection whilst plying their trade. From this it was deduced that, if the woman was dead when Crow saw her, she must have been killed between 2.10 a.m. and 3.30 a.m. Murder was so common in the area that very few observations on the condition of the body were made, nor were these backed up by any notes of temperature or rigor mortis, although the value of such information was even then well realised. Dr Timothy Keens, the police surgeon who examined the body, found some thirty-nine wounds in all, made up of nine stab wounds in the throat, seventeen in the region of the breasts and thirteen in the abdomen. He tentatively expressed the view that two kinds of weapons had been used: a long-bladed knife; and something very sharp, in the nature of a surgical instrument. He also said he thought that the assailant had some elementary knowledge of surgery and seemed to have been ambidextrous. He added, for good measure, that there may have been an attempt to give the impression of being left-handed. It was the unnecessary brutality and number of the wounds that distinguished the case from the usual drunken brawl which resulted in murder.

The police investigation into the background of Martha Turner showed that very little else was known about her except that, although she looked at least forty years old, she was believed to be only thirty-five, and had been a casual prostitute for some time, directing her operations from 4 Star Place, Commercial Road. She had last been seen alive in the company of a soldier in an alley not far away from the Angel and Crown at about 2.30 a.m. Somewhat naturally, the soldier immediately became a strong suspect – a suspicion which was enhanced because the police, in disagreement with the doctor (and, one suspects, without proper discussion) were convinced that the weapon used was a bayonet. The soldier was in due course identified and was able to prove that he had rejoined his unit at half past one, whilst other witnesses were certain that Turner returned to the Angel Public House at 1.40 a.m. and she had stayed there for some time.

At the inquest, held a week later by the Coroner, Mr George Collin, the 'usual' verdict of 'Murder by person or persons unknown' was returned. There the matter appeared to rest for the case was scarcely reported in the Press as there had been several other similar, isolated incidents in the area in the preceding months. Moreover, there seemed to be, in those days, no particular call for special action by the police and they appear to have pursued their enquiries little further. This was presumably because, as in the series of London prostitute murders of the last six years, there was little material evidence : no weapon, and no evidence of the man she must have met

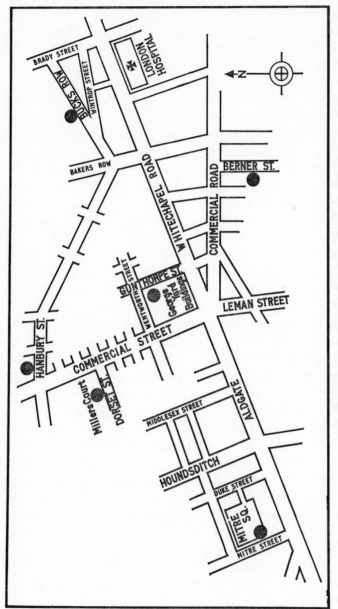

Jack the Ripper: plan of the sites of the murders

shortly before the murder. It would appear that in those days it was probably the usual course to discontinue enquiries in such circumstances. Today, when general records are kept, this is far from true and a good example is the 'Nude Girl' murders which have clearly occupied a vast amount of the time of experienced police officers.

The discovery of another victim on August 31st, under more dramatic circumstances, still failed to rouse much interest, although in this case both the finder of the body and the police were on the spot within a few minutes of the murder. It does not require a great deal of imagination to put oneself in the place of William Cross who, whilst walking down Bucks Row (Durward Street) at about 3.15 a.m., noticed, on the opposite side of the road, an object which looked like a piece of tarpaulin. As he came closer, he realised that it was a woman but presumed that she was drunk and had fallen down. Whilst he was still in the throes of deciding whether to leave her alone or try to revive her, he was joined by another man, John Paul, who said, 'She's dead drunk. Let's get her on her feet.' Groping about in the darkness, Cross suddenly noticed that she was bleeding from her throat and this was confirmed when they turned the body over and saw a pool of blood. Two very frightened men then ran full pelt down Bucks Row, straight into the arms of Haines, a policeman who was standing on the corner. Accompanied by another policeman who had joined them, the party went back to the scene, only to find that P.C. Neal (with a record of twenty years' service) had come from the other end and also discovered the body. He was quite certain that it had not been there half an hour before nor had he seen anyone when he was coming from Old Montague Street.

This lady was quickly identified by her clothes, which bore the stamp of the Lambeth Workhouse, as one of the same ilk as Martha Turner.

Mary – or Polly – Nicholls lived at 18 Thrawl Street, a

stone's throw from the site of the first murder. She was forty-two years old, and had left her husband and five children some seven years before. She had been seen at 2.30 that morning when she was wearing a new hat, was obviously drunk, and was standing in the Whitechapel Road, around the corner from her lodgings. The most inexplicable aspect of her case was that *nobody*, not even the police surgeon who was called, appears to have noticed at first the extent of the injuries. Moreover, before the post-mortem examination had been started, the mortuary attendant had undressed and washed the body, whilst the bloodstains in Bucks Row had also been washed away, even before the criminal investigation officers had arrived. At the Inquest, the Coroner – on this occasion a Mr Baxter – ventured to ask why the savage mutilation of the body[1] had not been noticed at the initial examination on the scene and whether the police had not, perhaps, realised that by removing the body to the workhouse before a thorough examination had been made vital clues might have been destroyed. On questioning the mortuary attendant, who proved to be a pauper from the local workhouse, the Coroner had little difficulty in discovering that he was obviously ignorant and untrained and had just followed the usual practice of stripping and washing the body, without giving the matter a thought.[2]

When asked whether the police were present when he undressed her he replied, 'No; only me and my mate Hatfield.' There is no doubt that *the police had certainly not told him to leave the body alone*. In fact, it is quite probable that they had given no instructions at all as to what he should do for he also made a very significant remark : 'Well, Sir, I did what was usual in these cases.' 'But surely

[1] Cut starting under left ear running to centre of throat – second cut starting halfway along this and running to right ear – two incised wounds running from lower abdomen upwards.

[2] This is still done in many hospital and public mortuaries and remains a strong argument even now for proper removal facilities by which continuity of evidence will be preserved.

you realised this was a case of murder?' said the Coroner. 'Oh yes. I shut up the mortuary and went and had my breakfast. When I came back, me and my mate undressed her and cleaned her up a bit and made her tidy.' 'Can you recollect if her clothes were torn?' 'They were torn and cut.'

In sharp contrast to his observations, the police seem to have been under the impression that the clothes had not been damaged and were quite emphatic that they *had given instructions* not to touch the body.[1]

The autopsy showed some similarities of the injuries with those of the previous case. The killing had clearly been accomplished in Bucks Row where the body was found, as there were no blood spots or drag-marks, and no traces of any vehicle. Yet, according to the witnesses, there was very little blood on the pavement, considering the extent of the wounds; but as the traces were washed off before any competent person could examine them, this leaves the possibility of the wounds being post-mortem still open to doubt. The doctor said that he found no signs of a struggle and a bruise on her face could have been caused by a hand held over her mouth to silence her. It was stated that the injuries were probably all inflicted by the same instrument, working from left to right and possibly by a left-handed person. The police had their own theory, as in the previous case, which was that she had been attacked from behind but this was not the view of the doctor. All this emphasises the impossibility of ever reaching any proper conclusion as to the truth of the case on mere hindsight.

The differences between the two cases lay chiefly in the degree of mutilation. In the first, the throat had not been

[1] In 1959 the body of a suspected case of murder, taken as usual to a hospital mortuary, was equally stripped and washed; whilst in 1932 the body of a man who had been quite clearly murdered by shooting, was taken from the scene without being photographed but later replaced for proper records to be made.

cut but in the second it was slit from ear to ear. In the first, there had been no deliberate mutilating cuts whilst the second had sustained extensive and possibly skilful cutting of the lower parts of the body, inflicted by a long-bladed, sharp weapon, such as a cork-gutter's or shoemaker's knife or even that used by a butcher, surgeon or mortuary attendant. All this must have been done within a maximum period of half an hour.

The victim-pattern continued, with yet another prostitute addicted to drink being murdered on Saturday, 8th September, this time at 29 Hanbury Street, a turning off the north end of Commercial Street. The house had a passage at the side which gave entrance to a small yard – almost ideally designed as a haunt for lovers and prostitutes. The discovery, as in the first case, was by a man, John Davis, who was on his way to work early in the morning. He lived with his wife in the top room and saw the woman lying close to the yard wall and assumed that she was drunk, a fallacy shared by the policeman he called. This assumption of intoxication, based on behaviour and the smell of the breath, has been a pitfall not limited to policemen.[1]

Inspector Chandler has the credit for realising that it was important not to interfere with the body and, whilst he was waiting for assistance, he inspected the scene and noted that there was relatively little blood in the yard, with a few bloodstains on the wall, close to the body, none being larger than a sixpenny piece. From this he concluded that the body had been dumped although careful examination of the passage showed no blood soiling and the proximity of the lower windows of the house to the passage made it seem impossible for anything to have been carried along it without having been heard. He noticed one bizarre feature; neatly placed at the feet of the woman, was a row of objects, consisting of two brass rings – which had been wrenched from the woman's middle finger – a

[1] See Manual of First Aid of St. John's Ambulance Brigade.

few pennies and two farthings, which had every appearance of having been arranged with care. Another possible clue took the form of a piece of bloodstained paper which had been torn off an envelope. This had the crest of the Sussex Regiment and was post-marked 'London, 28th August, 1888'. The part bearing the address was missing, with the exception of the letters 'M' and 'Sp' in writing. He also found two pills wrapped in paper. He noted also that the woman's clothing did not appear to have been torn. There was also a leather apron which, although saturated with water, showed no evidence of bloodstains.

Dr Bagster Phillips, who was called, examined the body before its removal, yet it was not until it had arrived at the mortuary that removal of a handkerchief which was wrapped around the neck revealed that the head had been almost completely severed from the body.

This third woman was identified as Annie Chapman, whose background was somewhat different from the others. She had been married to an Army Pensioner, a veterinary surgeon, who had come down in the world and found employment as a coachman. Some four years previously she left him and, for two and a half years until his death, he had continued to make her an allowance of 10/– a week. She had two children, one of whom was a cripple, and, since her husband's death when her allowance had ceased, she had had a struggle to exist. She was described as forty-seven years of age – but looked considerably older – five foot in height, plump, and well-proportioned with blue eyes and wavy brown hair. She was said to have had a remarkable addiction to alcohol, being frequently drunk. At 2 a.m. on the night of her death, she had been turned away from a common lodging-house because she had no money and, before this, she had virtually been starving. If true, then the money found at her feet must either have been given to her or contributed by the murderer. She had last been seen alive with a man outside 29 Hanbury Street, by a woman called Darrell. On this occasion, the police thought that the murderer must have been covered with blood, in spite of the absence of blood at the scene, and ignoring the possibility of post-mortem injuries.

At the Inquest, Mr Baxter was again the Coroner and he complained bitterly that he had no plan of the scene. Dr Phillips, the police surgeon, who had performed the autopsy, also protested about the difficulties under which he had carried out his examination, saying, 'I raise my protest as I have previously done that a member of my profession should not be expected to perform his duties in inadequate circumstances'.[1] The Coroner agreed with him that the body should have been taken to a proper mortuary and not to a shed, and that when the case was one of murder or suspected murder, a proper examination of the body was required which could not be carried out under such conditions. As on the previous occasions, the body had been stripped of its clothes and washed before it was examined by the doctor.

The pattern of autopsy findings appears to have been similar to that in the second case: the tongue was swollen, the throat had been cut twice, two front teeth were missing, and incisions on the body again suggested infliction from left to right. They were situated both on the front and the back, one being on the left side of the spine, for removal of the kidney. The ovaries had also been removed, an operation which, according to the doctor, indicated some anatomical knowledge, whilst the irregular nature of the cuts was explained on the basis of a person working in great haste. Recent bruises on the chin and sides of the jaw were suggested as being due to pressure having been applied to the victim's mouth. The Coroner returned the same verdict.

Two further murders which occurred about three weeks later brought the situation to one of acute panic, for they were committed on the same night, within about three

[1] See Chapter 10.

quarters of an hour, and about fifteen minutes' walking distance of each other.

The fourth woman was killed in a narrow court in Berner's Street which ran from Commercial Road towards the London, Tilbury and Southend railway. The entrance was a pair of gates with a small wicket gate which could be used when the main gates were shut. On each side high walls blotted out all light except at the far end of the yard which was overlooked by the windows of the International Workers' Education Club. The members had met, as usual, on Saturday, 29th September, for a debate on the necessity of socialism among Jews and this was followed by a concert at 11 p.m. The Steward of the Club, Louis Deimschutz, who worked as a porter in the daytime, arrived back with his pony and cart about 1 a.m., and had the utmost difficulty in persuading the pony to go in, although the gates of the courtyard were open. The animal, having seemingly taken an intense dislike to the right-hand wall of the court, refused to move beyond the entrance. Deimschutz therefore got down to discover the reason and, whilst poking around with his whip, found the body of a woman lying close to the wall. Making no attempt to search any further, he rushed into the Club with the news. Accompanied by one of the members, he returned to the body, which was still warm; although the clothes were wet from a recent shower, the ground beneath the body was dry, which suggested that death must have taken place a few minutes before his arrival. Some confirmation of this came from another member, William West, who had gone into the courtyard at 12.30 and had seen no body. Three doctors were called on this occasion : Dr Phillips, Dr Kay and Dr Blackwell. They arrived at 1.15 a.m. and estimated the woman had then been dead for not more than half an hour and possibly as little as twenty minutes. This woman was Elizabeth Stride (Long Liz), aged about forty-five, Swedish by birth, and – once again – a heavy drinker and a prostitute. She was dressed in a jacket of black diagonal cloth with feathered trimmings, a black skirt, velveteen bodice, crêpe bonnet and spring-sided boots with white stockings. She had in her pockets two handkerchiefs, a brass thimble and some black darning worsted, whilst in her right hand was a bunch of grapes, and her left hand held some sweets. Although her clothes were not disarranged, her bodice was open at the top and her throat had been cut in a similar manner to those of the others. Her body had *not* been mutilated, which was attributed to the murderer's having been disturbed. Almost before this information had been collected, the startling news was received that yet another female body had been found.

This woman was found in Mitre Square, which lies outside the district of the Metropolitan Police. P.C. Watkins of the City of London Police, made the discovery whilst on his beat there at 1.45 a.m. He had already passed the spot about a quarter of an hour before and seen nothing. On this occasion, his lantern shone on a woman's body lying in a pool of blood. So that, if the same person, the murderer had killed again within an hour, at about 1.30 a.m.

Despite facial injuries, this woman was recognised as Catherine Eddowes, about forty-five, who incredibly enough, had been under arrest at Bishopsgate Police Station earlier in the evening, on a charge of being drunk and disorderly, and had been released on bail at about 1 a.m. She must have met her assailant on her way between there and Mitre Square and possibly on his way from Berners Street.

The investigation of this murder revealed some curious information. The assailant would seem to have walked about a quarter of a mile to Dorset Street, where he washed some blood off his hands at a sink in an alleyway, and then wiped them on a piece of apron, which he dropped on the stairway of a house in nearby Goulston Street. There, on the wall of a passage, someone had written 'The Jewes are not the men to be blamed for nothing'. In addition, a bloodstained knife, with a ten-inch blade, was found in the Whitechapel Road (near the London Hospital); but Dr Phillips, who examined it, expressed doubt as to whether it was the weapon used.

Although the wounds inflicted on Eddowes were similar to those of Chapman, her predecessor that evening had her left ear torn in addition to her throat cut. This, and an oblique cut on Eddowes' right ear, suggested an association of the murderer with the writer of two letters to the Central News Agency. The first, received some days before these murders, was written in red ink and signed 'Jack the Ripper'. In it the writer promised more work in the near future and said that he would cut off the victims' ears and send them to the police. A second letter was received early on the morning of 1st October, which was before details of the murders were generally known. In it the writer explained that he had been disturbed, and hence was unable to send the ears as promised. A still more unpleasant communication was received by George Lusk, a local builder and member of the Whitehall Vigilance Committee, soon after this: it contained a human kidney, with an enclosure which said it had been taken from a woman. Half had been sent to him whilst the other half had been fried and eaten by the writer. In fact, Eddowes' left kidney *had* been removed and taken away. Dr Openshaw, Pathological Curator of the London Hospital Museum, examined the half kidney and is said to have concluded that it was a portion of kidney of a woman aged about forty-five, possibly an alcoholic, and that it had been removed within two weeks. He appears to have thought that it was not a practical joke, and the police were sufficiently interested to request that a comparison be made with the kidney removed at autopsy.[1] The 'postal' kidney was said to have one inch of the renal artery attached to it whilst

[1] The post-mortem was at Golden Lane (City of London) Mortuary.

two inches remained in the body. The autopsy kidney was stated to be in an advanced stage of Bright's Disease and Openshaw and Reed said that the kidney examined by them was in a similar state. Mr Sutton, a senior surgeon at the London Hospital who was an authority on the kidney and its diseases, gave as his opinion that the 'postal' kidney had been put in spirit within a few hours of its removal from the body.

In the general panic which ensued, the Commissioner of Police resigned, the police redoubled their efforts and the local tradespeople formed 'vigilantes'. In two months, death struck again. The victim this time was a younger woman, with a room of her own, and was generally more attractive and better off. On 9th November, the rent collector called at 13 Millers Court because the tenant, Mary Kelly, was in arrears with her rent. He found her door locked but, undeterred by this, because he thought she was avoiding him, he went round to the window, which he found to be broken, and pulled the curtains aside. He bitterly regretted his impetuosity for he was confronted with Mary Kelly's naked body – or what was left of it – lying on the bed. To say that it was mutilated would be an understatement, for parts of it had been cut off and strewn round the room, and even hung on the walls, yet once again her throat was cut. In contrast, a pile of clothes lay neatly at the foot of the bed, a feature common in sexual killings and related to the neat way in which the coins found near Chapman's body were laid out. This was certainly the first occasion on which the murderer had not been hampered by the risk of interruption, and he had made full use of his time.

The police were called and, on this occasion no less than four doctors performed the autopsy; this time the body was removed to Shoreditch mortuary. It would be satisfactory to record that a lesson had at last been learned, but it was only partly because of the previous unsatisfactory conditions. The real reason was to get the case

into a different Coroner's jurisdiction for both the police
and doctors had been embarrassed by the Whitechapel
Coroner's comments on the previous occasions and,
although Mr Baxter protested vehemently, it was to no
avail. The four doctors who performed the autopsy were
able to establish after six and a half hours that no parts
of the body were missing.

The Inquest, this time conducted by Dr MacDonald,
was rather less satisfactory from the point of view of the
public than previous ones. He not only cut short the
medical evidence but failed to question any of the witnesses, amongst whom were two who claimed to have seen
Kelly after 8 a.m. on the morning when her body was
found.[1] The inevitable verdict was returned by the
jury.

There were two interesting features in this particular
case, the first being that there was an eye-witness description of a man with whom Kelly had been seen in con-
versation at 3 a.m. at the corner of Millers Court. Now
eye-witness evidence may often not be very reliable, but
it may be that more significance can be placed upon it
on this occasion because of the immense publicity and
general fear and suspicion. On the other hand, it is impossible to rule out some stretches of imagination for he
was alleged to have been carrying a small thin parcel,
eight inches long, covered with American cloth and tied
up with a piece of string. This the witness obviously
thought was a knife. As a knife and its results had now
become a general obsession, it seems unlikely that any person who was indulging in such practices and with such
success would be likely to expose anything drawing attention to himself, not only to the public but to any potential
victim, when it would be quite easy to carry it inside the
leg of his trousers. Yet, as history has shown, success

[1] It must be noted that this was prior to the Coroner's Amendment Act, 1926, and the Coroner should have conducted a full
enquiry.

breeds over-confidence.

If the parcel is suspect then so, too, must be the description of a well-dressed man, 5 ft 6 ins in height, with dark complexion, dark eyes, bushy eyebrows and a thick moustache, in fact almost the stage villain. It is also said that he stood for several minutes talking to the girl whom he was contemplating taking to pieces, at an hour which could not fail but to attract attention.

The second matter of interest was the presence of burnt material in the fireplace. It seems to have been generally accepted that the clothes of the assailant must have been soaked in blood and, on this basis, it has been seriously suggested that he (or she) left wearing the victim's clothes, having burnt the soiled garments. Any theory as to blood-soiling of this kind must be viewed in the light of experience for it must depend upon several factors, not the least being whether the victim was dead or alive when any mutilation took place. There is also the possibility that the assailant might have been unclothed when performing his operation. As, however, little attempt appears to have been made to examine the material in detail, no information of real significance is available.

With this last and most sadistic of the series, the murders ceased as suddenly as they had begun. Theories and counter-theories as to who was responsible are a popular pastime and none of them, even the most plausible, comes remotely near any real degree of proof. A much more immediately urgent question justifies the research which has been devoted to Jack the Ripper. The police failed to identify or arrest the Ripper in 1888; would they, if he returned, do any better today? Although it is possible to point out many advances in the process of detection, both administrative and scientific, which have radically improved the position since the turn of the century, similar problems still remain unsolved, one of which is the sex murder. Nevertheless, it is worthwhile considering the question as posed above.

First and foremost, fingerprint identification as a practical science was not available to the London police in 1888. The possibility of identification by fingerprints had been realised by Dr Henry Faulds and Sir William Herschel, but even the improvements of Sir Francis Galton were not sufficient to make it of everyday use. It was an Argentine police officer, Juan Vucetich, who perfected the method of dividing the patterns of each print into a system of varieties. He achieved the distinction of being the first to solve a crime on fingerprint evidence in 1892. Within ten years, police forces throughout the world had recognised the potential of his work; and now palm-prints are equally valuable. Yet no real breakthrough has occurred other than in technique until the present day, when the chemical characteristics may be added as an additional weapon. The Ripper must certainly have left more than an adequate number of prints, on many of the items associated with the victims, whilst the letters (if genuine) might well have proved a modern forensic scientist's treasure trove. Trace evidence might have yielded dividends but certainly not if scenes of crime were approached in the same manner. Certainly a lot of dead wood could have been cleared away, as for example whether it was the murderer who washed his hands in the Eddowes case, for the blood should have been that of the victim. So, too, the knife found in the Whitechapel Road might have yielded evidence of blood or fingerprints.

Another specialty in which considerable progress has been made is that of handwriting identification, and the chemical analysis of ink and paper. The three letters in the case could certainly have either been exposed as unrelated, perhaps as hoaxes, or have yielded important clues. In association with fingerprint work, this aspect of the case should certainly not have remained so speculative.

The most unsatisfactory aspect of the case, that of the medico-legal facilities, would not necessarily have been so easy to criticise with complacency. In some places the conditions under which autopsies still have to be performed are little better than they were then, although much improvement has taken place in the last few years. Carelessness in the handling of the *corpus delicti* is still common, particularly when moved by untrained personnel who have been told it is a natural death. The approach of the doctors in all the Ripper cases appears to have been on the basis of accepting the obvious. Viewed in the light of other sadistic sexual murders, strangulation would usually be a very significant feature. It seems very possible that the Ripper silenced all his victims by strangling them for, in at least two cases, obstruction to the mouth is mentioned and the absence of bleeding is also a matter for comment. In all cases there was no sign or sound of a struggle, which tends to confirm this. Yet no effort was made to trace the typical injuries associated with this, with the result that the knife became at once the murder weapon and the means of mutilation. If this hypothesis were correct and had been realised, it is possible that the later victims might have escaped their fate, for throat-cutting is neither silent nor neat, whilst all prostitutes fear strangulation. To look for such marks is not a matter of inspired guesswork but a simple extension of the maxim that it is safer to proceed by excluding all possibilities than by taking the short cut of accepting what is obvious. It is a major and very dangerous temptation to find what is expected and look no further.

The singular lack of co-operation between the doctors and police – nay, even competition – in assessing the medical evidence is obvious for at no stage do they seem to have discussed it, except over the matter of the kidney, whilst in two cases there was development by the police of theories of their own which were quite irrelevant, if not contrary, to the doctors' findings. This can be said to have become a thing of the past. Although thanks to the efforts of such men as Chief Superintendent Salter there is an increasing effort to train police in the appreciation of scientific methods, there is still much to be taught in the objective assessment of scientific or medical evidence in cases of conflicting opinion or in giving them an idea of the reasoning and research involved. The attitude of many doctors to police work has not changed greatly, except where specialists are involved. The average general practitioner, usually inadequately trained in the subject, finds it very unrewarding, often very inconvenient, and unpleasant, both in practice and in working conditions. Little has been done to change this since the end of the last century; in fact there has been, in some universities, the retrograde step of discontinuing examinations in the subject, whilst postgraduate examinations attract little interest from those who adopt the attitude 'I know it all already'. Little has been done in the way of medical and scientific training for the police other than placing scientific laboratories in their midst and learning how to collect material whilst, for the forensic scientist, there is no organised training or instruction and little opportunity for fundamental research other than in the university.

The answer to one question 'Would Jack the Ripper have been caught today?' may well, on balance, be in the negative. He would have had a much more difficult time; but study of some of his modern counterparts shows that for some time at least they have more often than not eluded the police; and their downfall has been their own overconfidence. The nearest parallel has occurred in recent years in Sydney, Australia, among a similar class of person, the down-and-outs and drunks who have no settled home and frequent parks and dilapidated buildings. The only difference was that the victims were all male, but the type of attack and mutilation was closely paralleled.

The victim of the first murder was not a regular sleeperout but had gone to a dilapidated shed in a large park in the city to sleep off a drinking bout, having just quarrelled with the woman with whom he was living. This shed was a common haunt of deadbeats and stood close to a rock from which the man had frequently fished in the harbour. He had crawled underneath for shelter, and was found dead there with forty or more stab wounds in the head and neck. His genitals had been carefully, but not expertly, removed and were subsequently found by a police skin-diver in the water of the harbour. This removal had been done after death and there was no bleeding in the area involved. It was suggested that he was associating with homosexuals.

This was followed in November by a second, similar incident, the victim in this case being a deaf down-and-out aged thirty-seven years. After listening to the broadcast of a boxing match, he had gone to sleep in a toilet in a park nearby, again within a mile or so of the city. He had also been stabbed forty times and similarly mutilated after death. There was no known association between these two men.

After the first two incidents, a forensic psychiatrist forecast a repetition of them, which duly happened in March, 1962, when a man aged thirty-six years, known to be a heavy drinker, had left an hotel with a bottle of wine, apparently to go down a side street to continue his drinking bout, and was attacked in the open. Police patrols and fear had by then cleared the parks of people of this type and the would-be murderer was therefore forced into the open to obtain a victim. The open site might also account for the fact that the victim was still alive when found, and had only six wounds in the neck. The mutilation in this case had taken place before death and was therefore accompanied by sufficient blood spillage to make it almost certain that the assailant had been contaminated since not only had he been forced to work hurriedly, but was evidently disturbed before he could complete the murder.

The first two cases occurred on windy, wet nights but on the last occasion the weather was good. The assailant, if it is the same person, appears to be getting more confident and it is to be hoped more careless, but the attacks have not been repeated, and the shock of interruption in the last case may have deterred the murderer. Alternatively he may have been arrested on another charge or be in a mental hospital.

There are several parallels with the 1888 cases, besides the obvious one of type. The last case shows the assailant's growing confidence and carelessness, leading to an incident similar to the Ripper's fourth murder. Furthermore, police action, while forcing the murderer to change his habits (in this case from the parks to the open street; in the Ripper's, from side alleys to the prostitute's room), does not lead to any discoveries about the killer.

Yet, despite the availability of blood groupings, probably a stray fingerprint or partial impression of one, the murderer has not yet been found, and it does not seem likely that he will be. On the other hand, the attacks have ceased; but this is probably a question for the forensic psychiatrist to study, together with the problem of cyclical recurrence of the sadistic impulse. The psychiatrist cannot give much assistance to the police in the final analysis of identification of the individual, but studies of this type of crime should indicate the habits and record of the murderer. The blunt fact remains that the modern Ripper still escapes; and as our civilisation becomes even more complex, its pressures and problems may increase the incidence of such mentally sick men and women. Prevention would seem to offer more rewards than solution; for once the incipient signs of mental illness are more widely known and recognised as such, the treatment and cure will become easier.

Two more recent cases also apply: that of the West London Nudes and the Boston Strangler. In both of these cases, as in that of Jack the Ripper, the investigation is made more difficult by the fact that it is not always possible to identify all the cases as the work of one person. In the case of both Haigh and Christie, it was careless repetition which brought them to light, by which time the investigation had become of academic interest except for the purpose of presentation of evidence and the ultimate verdict of the trial – which depended upon the mental conditions of the accused. This does not mean that such cases do not fully justify a most detailed and thorough investigation, as with the Christie case and its bearing on Timothy Evans' trial.

One fact can be stated with almost one hundred per cent certainty. Although suggestions have been put forward connecting Jack the Ripper with similar incidents in other countries none of these are really very convincing. Sadistic killers of his type do not 'burn out' or 'retire' – hence the person involved after the perpetration of the last murder must have been out of circulation. There are only a limited number of ways in which this can happen – death, emigration or incarceration either in a prison or a mental hospital.

2 Quantities of Arsenic: The Maybrick Case

From the old-era terrors of the crowded, squalid streets of Jack the Ripper and the new-life down-and-outs in the open parks of the Sydney murderer, it is a far cry to the respectable working/middle-class streets of the suburbs of great towns. Yet the crimes peculiar to such districts – in so far as any crime is now limited or typical to any district – are even now in some respects more distasteful and unsettling than the grisly deeds of men sick in mind. The cold premeditation of murder by poisoning has flourished best in quiet areas where burglary was once an event that set the neighbourhood talking for weeks.

Poisoning, once suspected, might seem a much easier crime to detect; and so, in many ways, it is. But three major factors have militated against the conviction of its dispensers: the determination and secret planning involved, the character of the poisoner, and the problem of assembling adequate evidence and obtaining agreement on its significance from medical experts.[1] The first and last points will become amply clear in the two cases discussed; but that of character is perhaps at first more debatable. There has been much variation in the external appearances of those who have killed by poison; but it is noteworthy that almost all the central figures who have stood trial on such a charge have shown a coolness bordering on total indifference to their victim's fate and their own, a kind of misplaced stoicism. The popular legend that

[1] This is partly due to modern techniques making previous results not comparable.

poisoners have 'cold eyes' may have some truth in it; but it is well to beware of such emotional and far from logical arguments. In the first cases to be examined, the behaviour of the accused was almost the opposite of that of the popular image of the poisoner and was in fact adduced as evidence of her innocence. Innocent Florence Maybrick may have been; but her behaviour – at least until forensic psychiatry is much further advanced – cannot be a valid reason for thinking so.

The least spectacular way in which any murder can come to the attention of the public, that of suspicion of a death from apparently natural causes, is also the one likely to arouse the greatest controversy and emotion; for if the circumstances involve domestic intrigue in a familiar setting, members of the public will find it only too easy to identify themselves with the protagonists. It was the *Liverpool Daily Post* that originally brought the case to the attention of the public with its headline, on 15th May, 1899, 'Suspicious death of a Liverpool Merchant'; and this was followed up on the succeeding days by revelations calculated even in those days to excite interest in the minds of its readers. The gist of the *Daily Post*'s articles was that, while the dead man was well known in business circles, very little was known of his domestic life and it was hinted that some mysterious intrigue was involved.

In reality the beginnings of what was later to become a cause célèbre were hardly more than commonplace. Some eight years previously James Maybrick, a Liverpool cotton broker, had met in the course of his business travels in America, the daughter of a banker from Alabama, Florence Chandler, whom he married in 1881. The bride was scarcely eighteen and twenty-four years younger than the groom. After three years of travel, they settled in Liverpool where two children were born; and little appears to have been known of their domestic relationships which were to become a matter of such vital interest.

It was in March 1889 that signs of tension within the

household first appeared when some of the activities of James Maybrick, who was not entirely faithful to his wife, reached her ears. She, a woman in a strange land, consoled herself elsewhere, rather than turning to a friend for help, by having an affair with a man named Brierley. He still remains the mysterious figure in the case for he never gave evidence; the evidence of the days he spent in London with Mrs Maybrick being entirely reconstructed from witnesses. It seems that on 21st March, Mrs Maybrick left Liverpool for London, where she and Brierley spent three days at Flatman's Hotel, as Mr and Mrs Thomas Maybrick. Mrs Maybrick left London on the 27th, stayed with some friends, and only returned home on 28th March. The following day, she accompanied her husband on their annual excursion to the Grand National, there they met Brierley and Mrs Maybrick got out of her carriage and joined him. It was this that led to the quarrel which the prosecution later implied resulted in Mr Maybrick's death for, on their return home, there was a violent argument and James Maybrick gave his wife a black eye. With some difficulty she was persuaded to stay in the house and a bed was made up for her in the dressing-room. It was only some days later that the quarrel was resolved and her husband agreed to pay various debts which she had incurred without his knowledge.

So domestic relations were already strained at the end of the following month when the master of the house fell ill. He seems to have enjoyed excellent health till then, although it was generally believed that he was a hypochondriac – a diagnosis which had apparently been confirmed by his brother's doctor in London, a Dr Fuller who had found nothing more serious than indigestion. What his friends and acquaintances, including the doctor, had not known – it may be fortunately for his reputation – was that for many years he had been addicted to arsenic, to such an extent that he could assimilate a dose large enough to kill an ordinary man, without ill effect. One of the curious features of the evidence at the trial was that complete strangers came forward and gave full details of this habit, which may have been more aphrodisiac than hypochondriac in character, and yet his brothers were quite emphatic that he did not take the drug. It may be significant that Michael Maybrick admitted that he had questioned his brother after receiving a letter from Florence Maybrick, to which James had replied: 'Whoever told you that, it is a damned lie', and that this was in early April, about the time when he saw Dr Fuller in London.

Maybrick's illness began on 27th April and was attributed by him to an overdose of strychnine in some medicine he had brought back from London, coupled with a visit to Wirral Races, at which he had got very wet. His doctor, Dr Humphreys, after agreeing at first, then diagnosed chronic dyspepsia and put him on a diet, which brought rapid relief so that he was able to go to his office for the next three days. However, each day he felt slightly ill after lunch and on the evening of the third day was seriously ill. Dr Humphreys now diagnosed liver trouble, and tried various remedies, including a very weak solution of arsenic, in all about 1/25 grains. On 7th May, a second opinion was sought and a Dr Carter considered the acute dyspepsia to be due to an irritant in the stomach. Sedatives gave no relief and a nurse was obtained by Mrs Maybrick.

The following day, the backstairs suspicions which had been growing since the beginning of the master's illness reached ears outside the household, by way of Alice Yapp, the children's nurse. These suspicions centred on the fact that, about a fortnight before, Mrs Maybrick had been seen in her bedroom soaking fly-papers, which were known to contain poison. Alice Yapp told this to Mrs Briggs and Mrs Hughes, who were friends of the Maybricks, and, as a result, Michael Maybrick was summoned from London by a telegram which read: 'Come at once; strange things going on here.' Edwin Maybrick, who was already in the house, was also told by them, and Nurse Gore, who arrived that afternoon, was instructed that Mrs Maybrick was not to look after her husband in any way. Later that day, Alice Yapp produced new and more substantial evidence against her mistress in the shape of a letter she had been given to post that afternoon, and which was addressed to Brierley. It was in answer to one received from him on 6th May and in it she described her husband as 'sick unto death', underlining the words, in order to allay Brierley's fears that he might be making inquiries about their stay in London.

Until 11th May, when Maybrick died, all eyes were now on Mrs Maybrick. Apart from one startling episode, the various remarks she made were only of significance if her guilt was now assumed. On 9th May, Nurse Gore gave Maybrick some meat juice, which was removed by Mrs Maybrick soon afterwards and taken into the adjoining room. On her return, she tried unsuccessfully to persuade Nurse Gore to leave the room and left the bottle 'surreptitiously' on the table. This was sent for analysis and was found to contain half a grain of arsenic. On the following day, Maybrick was heard to say to his wife : 'Oh Bunny! Bunny! How could you do it? I did not think it of you!' He repeated this three times and Mrs Maybrick tried to calm him, telling him he must not worry but that she could not say what was the matter with him.

On Sunday, both before and after Maybrick's death, the house was searched with the avowed object of finding proof of Mrs Maybrick's guilt, which her brothers-in-law now considered established. As a result, a package marked 'Arsenic for cats' containing a very large quantity of the poison was found; and in two hatboxes were various articles associated with Maybrick's illness, all containing arsenic.

On this evidence, and that of the post-mortem, performed by the two doctors already concerned in the case and a Dr Brown, who considered the cause of death to be inflammation of the stomach and bowels by irritant poison, a death certificate was refused. At the Inquest on 5th June, the Coroner's jury gave a verdict that Maybrick had died from the administration of an irritant poison by Mrs Maybrick, with intent to take away life, with only two voices dissenting, and she was committed for trial at the next Assizes.

The only important evidence which had led to this verdict had been that of the doctors and of the analyst, which was at this stage unchallenged. But rumours and malice had been hard at work and the inclusion of Mrs Maybrick's name in the verdict appears to have been due not so much to any tangible proof, as to the atmosphere in Liverpool at the time, which seems to have been chiefly inspired by the sensational handling of the case by the local newspapers.

The advisers of Mrs Maybrick considered applying for the removal of the trial to London, on the grounds of local prejudice, but decided not to do so despite increasing rumours, many of which certainly emanated from members of the Maybrick household and family.

Sir Charles Russell appeared for the defence when the trial opened and the whole case hinged on two main issues : firstly, whether there was any motive; and, secondly, if death was due to poison, who had administered it. The first question largely dominated Mr Justice Stephen's charge to the grand jury in which he stressed Florence Maybrick's relations with Brierley as the probable motive for the crime and this was certainly open to criticism. Sir Charles Russell, whose moral principles were known to be strict, appears also to have chosen to accept this part of the prosecution's case with very little demur. Certainly the nature of the association, which was undoubtedly not of any long standing, was not emphasised; on the other hand, the letters of Mrs Maybrick were in a more passionate vein than those of Brierley. This was certainly thin ice for the defence but by all accounts the first issue of possible doubt was, to a great extent, left on one side by Sir Charles Russell.

The second issue on which the result of the trial largely hinged made great play of the question of Maybrick's addiction to arsenic. It was here that forensic medicine was of great importance and appears not to have exactly covered itself with glory. For the prosecution were called the three doctors who had performed the post-mortem and the analyst, but most important of all, Dr Thomas Stevenson of Guy's Hospital, who was the Home Office analyst.

The evidence of Doctors Carter, Humphreys and Barron was of interest, if not unusual, in one point, for none of them had suspected arsenic poisoning until two days before the patient died when Dr Humphreys was told by Mr Maybrick that 'there was something unsatisfactory'. The fact that neither had ever seen a case of arsenical poisoning, and general lack of suspicion, makes it not surprising that both Dr Humphreys and Dr Carter, in spite of regarding the symptoms as due to an irritant from some form of food or drink, hedged with 'acute dyspepsia', although after being told of the suspicions of the family, Dr Humphreys had tested samples of faeces on Thursday and had found no arsenic; he fell back on the excuse that he was not skilled in such matters. He also admitted that if poisoning had not been suggested to him, he would have accepted that death was due to gastritis or gastro-enteritis, a diagnosis which has occurred on other occasions. Finally, he said that there were no features of the post-mortem which distinguished the case from one involving these diseases.

Dr Carter, on the other hand, who had experience of cases of overdosing with arsenic, likewise had not suspected arsenical poisoning until he was handed the bottle of meat extract for analysis after Maybrick's death. Although quite positive that the fatal dose was administered on Tuesday, the 3rd, and that there had been subsequent doses, in cross-examination he agreed that the distinction between the symptoms of arsenical poisoning and irritant food poisoning were very slight and that certain expected and recognised signs, such as bloodshot eyes, were absent. Furthermore, the symptoms had appeared after an unusually long interval following administration of the fatal dose.

Dr Barron, who also attended the post-mortem and had had wider experience of arsenical poisoning, could say no more than that the changes which actually caused death probably arose from irritant poisoning and also that some of the symptoms normally associated with arsenic poisoning were absent. This theme was taken up by Dr Thomas Stevenson, an accepted authority, who insisted that the general symptoms corresponded to irritant mineral poisoning. Yet, in cross-examination however, he was remarkably vague about his previous experience of post-mortems on such cases, especially when the traces of arsenic were only revealed by analysis. He was, however, quite definite that habitual taking of arsenic could not produce even the small amount (0.02 of a grain in six ounces, which was reckoned to represent 0.125 of a grain in the whole liver) found unless taken shortly before death in almost fatal doses. His evidence completed the case for the prosecution.

For the defence, Sir Charles Russell called two witnesses, who spoke of Maybrick's habit of taking arsenic while in America some seven years before, and a chemist who had dispensed liquor arsenicalis to be taken up to seven times a day. In addition, he also called two medical experts who had wide experience of arsenical poisoning and who did not consider that Maybrick had died of it. Dr Tidy, who had examined over forty cases of it in the previous few years, pointed out that there was an absence of certain other usual symptoms, which had already been admitted by Dr Stevenson, and also dealt in some detail with the inaccuracies inherent in the method used for determining the arsenic present in the liver. Finally, he cited two cases where arsenic administered medicinally had produced similar analytical results which definitely had no relation to the cause of death. In the present case, the actual quantity found was .082 gr; in these cases, .028 and .174 gr respectively had been found, and in neither case was arsenic poisoning the cause of death. In this case, he considered that death was due to gastro-enteritis.

The other medical witnesses were Dr Macnamara, who claimed to be one of the few people in the world who had at that time administered the drug to saturation point, and both he and Professor Paul agreed about the absence of certain symptoms that chronic dyspepsia coupled with Maybrick's soaking at Wirral Races could have weakened his stomach to a point where gastritis would be fatal.

The most dramatic moment of the trial was yet to come; for although the prisoner in those days could not give evidence on her own behalf, she could make a statement from the dock. This Mrs Maybrick chose to do and explained the presence of arsenic in the meat essence as follows:

'My Lord, I now wish to refer to the bottle of meat essence. On Thursday night, the 9th May, after Nurse Gore had given my husband beef tea, I went and sat on the bed beside him. He complained to me of being very sick and depressed and he implored me to give him this powder, which he had referred to earlier in the evening, and which I had declined to give him. I was overwrought, terribly anxious, miserably unhappy, and his evident distress utterly unnerved me. He had told me that the powder would not harm him and that I could put it in his food. I then consented... When I found the powder, I took it into the inner room, with the beef juice... On returning to the room, I found my husband asleep, and I placed the bottle on the table by the window... As he did not ask for the powder again, and as I was not anxious to give it to him, I removed the bottle from the small table where it would attract his attention, to the top of the washstand, where he could not see it. There I left it, my lord, until, I believe, Mr Michael Maybrick took possession of it.'

Since the defence had until now rested on the medical evidence that Maybrick did not die of arsenic poisoning, Sir Charles Russell was now in a dilemma and he chose not to emphasise this aspect but reverted to the previous argument, using Mrs Maybrick's statement only with reference to the presence of arsenic in that one place. He did not make it by any means clear that this was a perfectly reasonable defence and so, in some of the jurymen's minds, there may well have been a feeling that he was saying 'We deny that arsenic was a possible cause of death; but if it was, it was administered at Maybrick's request'. Mr Justice Stephens, in his summing up, again stressed to excess the motive provided by adultery, an argument which the defence had made little attempt to demolish for the only possible line, that although adultery is wrong, yet it is not necessarily a cause for murder, was not exactly one for any advocate (let alone a Roman Catholic) to be expected to adopt at a time when it was considered an unforgivable *social* sin. Planned and premeditated adultery was enough to prejudice any jury and it may well be that this influenced the jury's verdict in the end. The judge certainly expressed himself strongly on this point, whilst on the other hand, he seemed to dismiss rather readily the medical evidence as being only partially important, speaking of 'subtle partisanship' and 'readiness of skilled witnesses to become advocates' in cases such as this. It is of interest that, whilst he was quite prepared to accept the evidence that Sir Charles Russell had produced which showed Maybrick's addiction to arsenic, in his closing words he again tended to lay emphasis on the circumstantial aspects of the case, thereby evincing the whole of judicial suspicion of the expert.

There are certainly three or four matters in the case which reveal circumstances of very grave suspicion and which, as in any other indictment for murder, must be considered independently of chemical and medical evidence. It is these which evoke suspicion and require corroboration from other sources or may themselves corroborate other evidence.

It was in other ways an unsatisfactory summing up, avoiding the issue of reasonable doubt entirely, and dwelling on reasonable probability; but that is for a lawyer to criticise. The jury were only out for thirty-five minutes before returning a verdict of guilty.

There was no Criminal Court of Appeal to which the case could be referred and only a petition obtained a last-minute reprieve. The grounds given, however, were somewhat illogical for it might well have been a pardon, since it substantially rested on the defence's main argument :

'The Home Secretary, after fullest consideration, and after taking the best legal and medical advice that could be obtained, has advised Her Majesty to respite the capital sentence on Florence Maybrick, and to commute the punishment to penal servitude for life, inasmuch as, although the evidence leads clearly to the conclusion that the prisoner administered and attempted to administer arsenic to her husband with intent to murder, yet it does not wholly exclude a reasonable doubt whether his death was in fact caused by the administration of arsenic.'

As *The Times* commented the following day :

'It makes all things comfortable all round.'

In this field at least adequate progress has been made to prevent similar dubious verdicts. The scientific evidence of the prosecution as presented by analysts and doctors is certainly open to criticism; they seem to have tested for the presence of arsenic and, on finding it, have made little effort to discover other possible sources. One such source, besides the glazing which the defence had analysed, was the zinc used in Marsh's test, the method of tracing arsenic employed at the post-mortem. Since Mrs Maybrick was convicted on the cumulative evidence of arsenic traces, each individual item should have been examined with much greater care.

It is interesting to note that one of the first cases of arsenical poisoning to be tried after the institution of the Court of Criminal Appeal, and after the defendant was allowed to give evidence, resulted in a verdict of guilty largely based on the defendant's behaviour in the witness box. The trial of the Seddons in December 1911, for murdering their lodger Eliza Barrow, by arsenic poisoning, was scientifically unremarkable, the organs containing arsenic in small but well-distributed quantities. The only point of doubt which was raised concerned the multiplication factor involved in the estimation of the actual quantity administered as opposed to that recovered; but on this Dr Wilcox was unshakable.

This trial differed from that of Mrs Maybrick because, in the Maybrick case, whilst there was an abundance of evidence of arsenic being available for the accused, at no time was there any proof offered that Seddon had had arsenic in his possession; in fact, the only reasonable theory as to its source came from Seddon himself. It is unlikely that the jurors really believed in the fly-papers story; it had certainly met no success as a theory of provenance in the Maybrick case. They were merely the commonest of many domestic articles which in those days contained the poison. It may well have been Seddon's cool and calculating behaviour and the way in which he was more interested in the monetary details than in the events leading up to Miss Barrow's death that contributed to his conviction.

With the improvements in the standards of post-mortem examination in suspected cases of poisoning, some of which have resulted from bitter experience in the past, combined with the advances of analytical techniques, it is unlikely once a case of poisoning is suspected that scientific evidence will be at fault. Moreover, with the safeguards afforded to the defence by the Coroner's Rules (1953) from the pathological aspect, and the opportunity for cross-checking results from the analytical point of view, there should be no conflict other than in interpretation. On this account it can be fairly confidently said that there should be no reason for anxiety in the minds of the public, such as existed as a result of the Maybrick case.

Lest the foregoing statement should give rise to the same false sense of complacency which has existed for the last fifty years, it is as well to appreciate that, with the development of new standards of analysis goes hand-in-hand new methods of synthesis and hence new poisons, some of which may produce symptoms not generally recognised; whilst others may be extremely difficult, if not impossible, to recover by analytical methods, either because they are broken down in the body or because there is no known method of identification. As yet, the recognition and estimation of the breakdown products (metabolites) is often a difficult problem and herein lies some of the future of toxicology. In the same way as, in a different context, the admission that there was too little blood to group may have led to a failure to arrive at the truth, so a similar statement that the presence of a small quantity of a poison might represent a much larger quantity, could lead to a parallel situation, especially if the scales of circumstantial evidence were heavily weighted against the accused. However, in view of the small numbers of cases of homicidal poisoning which come to light each year, this is of little significance compared with the possibility that there are cases of murder by poisoning which are not even suspected. This has not been overlooked as anyone who has read the book on *The Detection of Secret Homicide* by Havard[1] will know. A careful study of the problem will suggest that the reason is not very different from that revealed in the Maybrick case, when it was a matter of comment that none of the doctors appeared to have thought of poison until their attention was drawn to it by someone else. In those days of servants, there *was* someone else; but times have changed and the presence of outside observers is less whilst the level of suspicion amongst the medical profession is

[1] London 1960.

certainly no greater. In addition, the social relationship between doctor and patient is slighter. This lack of grounds for suspicion is a matter for critical consideration, but the fact remains that every year there are large numbers of deaths from poisoning which have escaped the notice of doctors who have certified that death has taken place or have even been in attendance on the patient; had it not been for the vigilance of the Coroner and the pathologist, these cases would have escaped notice. Some of these could have been homicidal but by the time they have been discovered little evidence is likely to remain if an interval of time has elapsed; whilst there may be other bodies which have been certified as having died of natural disease and disposed of as such. It may be that this is in part due to inadequate medical education, both undergraduate and postgraduate, in the art of observation and suspicion aided by the feeling in certain academic quarters that forensic medicine should have no place in the curriculum, an attitude which changes rapidly when an individual finds himself concerned.

3 Crippen and Christie

So far, the cases which have been discussed have fallen into two types. In the first, the chain of supposed motive – victim – criminal was incomplete because the identity of the assailant or assailants has never been discovered; in the second, the chain was complete and only the necessary evidence was needed; but many crimes come under a third heading, where motive and criminal seem adequately certain, while the victim's identity or fate become the central problem of the case.

Most murderers are fully aware that the old rule 'no body, no murder' usually holds good, and some make an attempt to hide or otherwise dispose of the body. As a result the victim will merely disappear from the neighbourhood. It is inevitable therefore that from time to time the police will be presented with the whole or parts of a body, sometimes after a time-lapse which even amounts to years and often in a far from fresh condition. The problem is then reduced to one of proving the identity of the person and of showing that death was due to violence. It is worth noting that very rarely has a defence of accidental death succeeded where the body has been concealed.[1] This may be because juries are inclined to assume that a death which requires concealment of the body implies that there was something else to conceal. The reason which naturally comes to mind is murder. Such an appraisal is clearly

[1] One of the very rare exceptions was the Rhyl Mummy case (*Reg. v. Harvey* [Rutland Assizes, 1960]) where a woman was acquitted of the murder of her lodger whose body was found in a mummified state with a stocking round its neck twenty years after death.

51

based on circumstantial evidence but may disregard weakness in the scientific evidence. Indeed it has been said that Marshall Hall, who refused the brief for the defence in the case of *Rex v. Crippen* (1911),[1] suggested that the line of defence should be that the victim had died from an accidental overdose of hyoscine, administered to her as a sexual depressant since her demands upon her husband, who also had a mistress, were exorbitant. It would have been interesting to see what effect such a line of defence would have had on the jury, especially as there is reason to believe that further inquiry into the technique used to isolate the drug (about which very little was known at the time) would have shown that it was not satisfactory.

In the event, the first fascination for the general public in the case of *Rex v. Crippen and Le Neve* was that the arrest of the accused was the first in which wireless telegraphy was used to apprehend the murderer. On 22nd July, 1910, Captain Kendall of *SS Montrose*, on a voyage from Amsterdam to Quebec, sent a long telegraph message to his owners, describing two passengers who seemed to correspond to the description of two persons wanted for questioning with reference to the suspected murder of Mrs Cora Crippen. These were her husband, Dr Hawley Harvey Crippen, an American from the Middle West who had been resident in England for ten years, and his paramour and former secretary, Miss Ethel Le Neve.

For nine days, Captain Kendall watched the pair, who were travelling under assumed names, with Miss Le Neve in boy's attire; and he was careful to let no hint of his suspicions escape, until the police officer in charge of investigations was able to overtake the *Montrose* by sailing from Liverpool with a colleague. They boarded Captain Kendall's ship on 31st July and brought Crippen and his

[1] The suggestion is stoutly repudiated by Sir Travers Humphreys in *A Book of Trials* (London, 1953).

companion back to England to face a much publicised trial.

It was the most gruesome aspect of the prosecution's case – that there was nothing that could be readily described as an identifiable body – that gave the case its continuing interest. All that the police surgeons had to work on were some dismembered remains from which all major identifying features were missing. The case rested *prima facie* on three facts: that Mrs Crippen had not been seen since 1st February, when she was purported to have gone to America, where she had become seriously ill and died. However, Crippen then aroused suspicion by bringing Miss Le Neve, already his mistress, to live with him at his house in Hilldrop Crescent. Gossip increased after Miss Le Neve appeared at a dinner dance wearing Mrs Crippen's jewellery three weeks after the latter's disappearance. But it was not until 30th June that a Mr Nash finally went to Scotland Yard. Mrs Crippen, or Belle Elmore, had many friends and acquaintances among music-hall singers, and the latter made active inquiries of Crippen as to her whereabouts. Crippen wrote letters consistent with the story of his wife's death in America. If Crippen had not been so hasty in replacing his wife by Ethel Le Neve, Belle's friends might well have forgotten the slight mystery attached to her disappearance; but the coincidence of the two events was too much for them.

As a result of the information received, Inspector Dew of Scotland Yard[1] called on 8th July, on Crippen who was most helpful, and placed no obstacles in the way of the police, co-operating with them in a full search of the house. He said that Mrs Crippen was not, to the best of his belief, dead, but had left him abruptly on 1st February. He did not know where she had gone, and had put about the story of her death to save embarrassment to himself. Inspector Dew was with Crippen throughout the day, and at the end of his inquiries and search was fully satisfied

[1] As a young man, Dew assisted in the Ripper investigations.

that there was nothing more in the case of any material importance.

But Crippen's outward calm belied an inward terror which was to prove his undoing. By Sunday 10th July, he and Ethel Le Neve, the latter in her boy's disguise, were in Antwerp awaiting a passage on the *Montrose*. Yet even now, when his nerve had in effect broken, the arrangements he made for his departure were as meticulous as ever, and as considerate for his colleagues as possible. Indeed, if it had not been that Inspector Dew had returned on the Monday to Crippen's office to clear up a few minor points, to find, quite contrary to his expectations, that the doctor was no longer there, the crime might yet have been recorded as a case of disappearance. Instead, the inspector immediately suspected deeper complications, and searched the house at Hilldrop Crescent again. It was not until a further search was made on 13th July that his tenacity was rewarded. As he tested the floor of the cellar to see whether the bricks were loose, he found an area where they did appear to have been disturbed. Digging brought to light what was clearly part of a human body, without bones or head. There were also present a pyjama jacket, part of a woman's undergarment and some hair curlers. The subsequent publicity lead to the arrest of Crippen and Le Neve.

The problems from the scientific point of view were firstly identification and second by the cause of death. The identification was dependent upon visual recognition of the undergarment as that worn by the missing woman, visual identification of the pyjama jacket as matching (in pattern and threads) a pair of trousers found elsewhere in the house and subsequently shown to be one of three sets. These could not have been manufactured before 1908 and had been bought after January 1909 and worn since then. The curler had hair attached to it which was similar in colour to that of Mrs Crippen (which had been dyed). Finally it was known that Mrs Crippen had a scar on the abdomen following an ovarectomy. The medical experts, who included Dr Pepper and Bernard Spilsbury, expressed the opinion that there was a scar on a portion of skin from the abdominal wall. This completed the case from the point of view of identification. In addition, Dr William Willcocks found hyoscine in the remains, and the last link in the outline was filled in when it was found that Crippen had ordered hyoscine on 17th or 18th January from a chemist in Oxford Street, and had on 18th January collected 5 grains of the drug, signing the poisons register with his name and business address.

In the meantime the solicitor for the defence had approached Dr Turnbull who was director of the Bernhard Baron Institute of Pathology at the London Hospital for an opinion on the validity of the alleged scar. He did this with the assurance that such an opinion would not require Turnbull to give evidence and on this assurance Turnbull examined the material and expressed the definite opinion that the alleged scar was in fact merely a fold in the skin. This was based on histological sections. The solicitor, contrary to his original promise, subpoenaed Dr Turnbull and other experts to give evidence at the trial; against their better judgment, for the prosecution knew about the original agreement. Turnbull was asked to express an opinion outside his own speciality on the source of the muscle which was attached to the scar. It was the cross-examination on this matter and the presence of aponeurosis which was demonstrated in court that virtually destroyed the weight of the evidence against identification as a scar. As this will always be a matter of controversy it was a great pity that the actual scar reserve tissue was destroyed as recently as a few years ago, before it could be re-examined. At the present time it is unlikely that any problem would arise, because using techniques of photography with reflected ultra violet light it might have been possible to provide a permanent record and not only identify scars but age them.

However as writers have expressed an opinion (but retracted it in discussion) that Turnbull was dishonest it is only proper to put on record that he had in fact not only a reputation throughout his life for the highest professional integrity but was probably one of the greatest morbid anatomists of the first half of this century, one whose opinion was sought all over the world. For this reason it seems rather surprising that his opinion should be so lightly dismissed, based as it was on several specific observations. It does however draw attention to the practice now in force of experts examining the material together before the case, which has obviated clashes of opinion on facts in court. From examination of this aspect of the case it seems probable that Turnbull was pressed into an opinion on the anatomical aspect with which he was not fully conversant and had his mind completely fixed on the 'scar' to which he had given a great deal of study. It certainly affords a good example to those without experience that cross-examination in a criminal court of law is not the same as an academic discussion where not only the technical standard may be higher but the ease of repartee is certainly greater.

Under modern scientific scrutiny the hair might have been more closely identified by comparison with samples of hair of Mrs Crippen which should have been found in the house; but otherwise as a criminal investigation, the case would bear comparison with the best modern methods from the point of view of thoroughness, and it is of interest that Dew himself in his book obviously resents a report of the trial which records him as saying that he did not take any further specific steps after 14th July, commenting that if that had been so the fugitives would never have been convicted.

While the Christie case did not depend entirely on the establishment of one identity, the reconstruction of the bodies of his earliest victims shows how far this particular branch of forensic science has advanced. It also illustrates in certain aspects the great potential of scientific investigation but thereby underlines the slowness of its adoption in other directions.

It was in 1938 that John Christie took the lease of the ground floor flat at 10 Rillington Place in an area of West London that in many ways parallels Whitechapel to the east, except that it was once an eminently respectable neighbourhood which has since declined, and now, for various reasons, occupies as much of the time of the police as did the East End in Jack the Ripper's day. Rillington Place itself is a cul-de-sac, and Number Ten stands at the end, on the left-hand side. In many places it is the kind of house where neighbours would hardly fail to comment on any strange occurrence, but here, where anonymity is a most desirable quality, evil is neither seen nor heard. Christie himself seemed respectable enough, and served as a war reserve policeman with great efficiency and some petty tyranny, although he himself had committed minor offences. However his real claim to fame in 1953, when the present story opens, was his appearance at the Old Bailey as the star witness in the trial of Timothy Evans for the murder of his child in the same house.

The events which started the investigation were undramatic enough. In March 1953, Christie sold his furniture, saying that he was moving to the North, where his wife had gone to await him; he sublet his flat, taking three months' rent in advance from a young couple. The landlord, however, arrived on 21st March, and quickly disillusioned them as to Christie's right to sublet. He dispossessed them, and found new tenants. It was one of the latter who on 24th March had the unpleasant experience of finding the traces of the previous occupant's

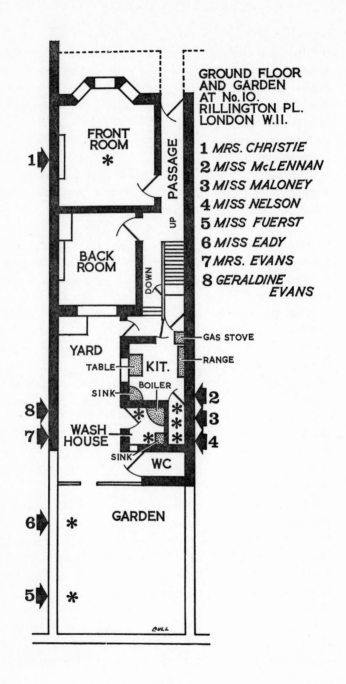

GROUND FLOOR
AND GARDEN
AT No. 10.
RILLINGTON PL.
LONDON W.11.

1 MRS. CHRISTIE
2 MISS McLENNAN
3 MISS MALONEY
4 MISS NELSON
5 MISS FUERST
6 MISS EADY
7 MRS. EVANS
8 GERALDINE
    EVANS

FRONT
ROOM
*

PASSAGE

UP

BACK
ROOM

DOWN

GAS STOVE

YARD

TABLE

KIT.

RANGE

SINK

BOILER

WASH
HOUSE

SINK

WC

GARDEN

*

*

GULL

activities when he was attempting to fix a wireless set. To do this, he pulled off the wallpaper at the far end of the kitchen and uncovered a door which had one corner missing. Through this gap he shone a torch which showed the naked back of a woman. His telephone call to the police brought into action the usual investigation procedure; for this was still – and in retrospect it seems a masterpiece of understatement – no more than a question of 'Woman's body found in cupboard'. The Coroner was immediately notified by his officer, while the Criminal Investigation Department of Notting Hill Police Station were on their way to the scene under the capable direction of Detective Chief Inspector Griffin.[1] They were shortly joined by all the necessary specialists whom he had at his disposal, including photographers, forensic science officers, and a pathologist instructed by the Coroner.

What followed was routine procedure. The photographer, Detective Superintendent Percy Law of Scotland Yard, took photographs of the room as it appeared before the cupboard was opened. When this was completed, and the pathologist had arrived, the cupboard was photographed before any of its contents had been disturbed and after this at each stage of the operation so that a complete permanent record of the evidence was obtained, both in its original state, and after it had been handled.

It was at this point that the case became really unusual. What had started as one woman's body in a cupboard proved to be three. All were well preserved, putrefaction and the accompanying smells being minimal, due in part to a circulating current of dry air. Two were wrapped in blankets. Further search of the house showed that the floorboards of the front room appeared to have been disturbed and on removing them between the joists was found another body, which, as in the case of those in the cupboard, was also of a woman and wrapped in a blanket. In this case, as post-mortem changes were more marked,

[1] Later Chief Superintendent.

death seemed to have taken place considerably earlier and the woman was older.

The first three bodies were removed to the Kensington mortuary[1] where the autopsies were performed the same evening. From these emerged a mass of information, which showed quite clearly what type of crime was involved. All three bodies found in the cupboard bore evidence of ligature strangulation with carbon monoxide in the blood as well as of sexual intercourse at about the time of death. The dates of death were estimated as up to four weeks and about eight weeks and up to twelve weeks prior to discovery. The body found under the floorboards which was examined the next day showed only evidence of strangulation and had been there for at least about three months.

When, on the following day, the police resumed their investigation a complete examination of the house was carried out. It was not until 27th March that examination of the garden revealed what appeared to be human bones, some in an old bonfire, as well as a femur (thigh bone) which had been used to prop up some trellis work. It was at this point that previous experience indicated a special routine collection. The remains of the bonfire (part of a dustbin) were carefully removed to the police laboratory where it was sifted, as were various suspicious fragments of bone which were collected from the garden, which had been divided into plots.

The bones which were identified as a result of this work were taken to London Hospital Medical College, where a team of anatomists, working under Professor Richard Harrison were able to establish that they represented the skeletal remains of the bodies of two women and that from one the skull was missing. The other information can be summarised:

[1] The Royal Borough of Kensington Mortuary was where the bodies of Mrs Evans and her daughter were examined originally by Dr Teare.

	SKELETON A	SKELETON B
Skull :	Burnt and fragmented	Missing
Vertebrae : C1	Burnt – articulated well with skull A	Unburnt – poor articulation with skull
C2	Burnt – articulated well with C1 of A, not with C1, or C3 of B	Missing
C3	Burnt – articulated with C2 of A	Unburnt – did not articulate with C2 of A
C4	Missing	Missing
C5	Unburnt – articulated with C6 of set 1 below	
Set 1 – C6, C7, T1 articulating with C5		Set 2 – C6, C7, T1 did not articulate with C5 of set

In the meanwhile, although the first few days of the search had yielded all the above evidence, and various other minor items, the police had decided that the surface soil of the whole garden must be examined. The plan dividing the garden into plots was used again, and one by one each area was dug over and sifted to a depth of eighteen inches, despite rain which turned the loam into an unworkable mass. The patience of the workers was rewarded when on the last day the fourth cervical vertebrae was found. This was unburnt, and articulated with C3 of Skeleton B, but not with C5 of set 1. Hence the skull belonged to Skeleton A, as did set 1 of the lower vertebrae. Thus the important piece of dental evidence obtained from the skull, a mental dental crown of foreign origin, belonged to the younger and taller of the two women.[1]

At the inquests, it proved possible from records and descriptions to identify both of the bodies that had been buried in the garden. The first skeleton was that of Ruth Fuerst, an Austrian refugee first reported missing on 1st September, 1943. The height, age, and sex were the same, which along with the presence of the German palladium silver alloy dental crown fitting in with her Austrian nationality, was regarded as adequate evidence. The second skeleton proved to be that of Muriel Eady, who although reported missing on 4th November, 1944, had not in fact been seen since 7th October of that year. Again the height and age and sex were the same, and in addition there were fragments of clothing and some head hair which was similar to samples recovered from her clothing at her home.

When Christie himself was arrested on 31st March he admitted responsibility for the deaths of all the women concerned. With Christie's confession the case against him was now virtually complete, especially as it included information which fitted in with the findings. One feature of this part of the case was that Christie was an exceptionally co-operative witness against himself, and very ready to talk about his activities which may be explained by a remark he made later (possibly with a view to establishing insanity): 'The more the merrier'. Unfortunately not all that he said was true and hence anything which could not be corroborated in full had to be regarded as suspect. As a general rule, any such evidence

---

[1] Information later supplied by Christie showed that a skull found at 133 St Martin's Road in 1949 (at the same time of the Evans murder) belonged to the other skeleton. This had been examined by a pathologist at the time but had not seemed to warrant a full study, although he did express the opinion that it was the skull of a woman about 32 years old who suffered from nasal catarrh. It was destroyed and recorded as an air raid casualty.

has to be viewed in consideration of the fact that the murderer does not want to lose too much self-esteem.

He made in all three voluntary statements between 31st March and 8th June. In them he described the various murders in very similar terms to those reconstructed by the police, and they read as a story of cold-blooded factual information. It is by comparison of these statements with the detailed scientific investigation that the accuracy of the latter can be assessed, bearing in mind that Christie commenced by saying that he would tell as much as he could remember allowing presumably for any discrepancies by the fact that 'he had not been well for a long time, about eighteen months'.

In the case of his wife, he first excused himself on the grounds that he woke up on 14th December, to find her convulsing and choking with her face blue. He tried to restore her breath, but failed, and since he believed it too late to call for assistance, he said 'I got a stocking and tied it round her neck, and put her to sleep'. After he had done it, he noticed a cup half full of water and a bottle containing two phenobarbitone tablets which had originally contained twenty-five; in his own words 'I knew she must have taken the remainder'. Having thought for two days what to do with the body he finally moved a table, rolled back the linoleum and lifted the floorboards in the front room. He had wrapped her in a blanket and put her body in between the joists where the pipes had recently been mended. He then covered her with rubble and replaced the boards and lino. The routine analysis which had been carried out for material collected at autopsy showed no barbiturate.

His description of the death of his next victim also appears to be an attempt to justify himself, for he says that she accosted him in a drunken state and threatened to creae a scene if he did not take her home. She then forced her way into his house, and when he was trying to get out to avoid her she attacked him with a frying-pan.

He grappled with her and must have lost his head, because the next thing he remembered was finding her with a rope round her neck, lying in a chair (the murderer's classical statement – 'Everything went black'). He went to bed, and found her in the same position in the morning. Nor did he remember putting her in the cupboard and throwing her clothes in afterwards. To do this, he had to admit that he must have performed certain active operations. He made no mention of sexual intercourse, and explicitly stated that it was because he would not indulge in it that she became abusive. There was no mention of gas. Both these factors had appeared in the medical and scientific examination.

His last statement, three days later, dealt mainly with Mrs Evans, with which we are not basically concerned for many have devoted much time to this case.[1] However, he added some remarks at the end which are of interest, because he now admitted gassing some of his victims before strangling them. This, in one case, he said he did by attaching a tube to a gas pipe on the wall near the window, and letting the end hang down behind the chair. This at least (if correct) confirmed the pathological finding of carbon monoxide poisoning in these cases.

The confessions made by Christie are an excellent illustration of two vital elements in this study. One is that a good investigating police officer can be remarkably accurate and detailed in his collection of evidence and shows how it is possible to recover an amazing amount of detail despite the passage of time. The descriptions and identifications of Christie's first two victims are outstanding examples of what really systematic, properly controlled and directed scientific examination can yield when closely associated with good police investigation. It is not skill alone which determines the fruitfulness of this type of

---

[1] It might have been better if they had examined the case with less emotional involvement.

work, but the effectiveness of the man directing operations. Anything which tends to diminish that effectiveness, whether it be shared responsibility or lack of training in the assessment of the relative factors involved, should be avoided as far as humanly possible.

On the other hand, whether from genuine mental confusion – excusable enough in a man in his position – or from a desire to present himself in the best light he could, Christie suppressed or only recalled later many details which the police had already uncovered. Curiously enough, he was quite open about his earliest crimes, where no amount of research would have revealed the full details of his activities. It is at this level, where the combination and evaluation of confession and evidence is crucial, that something in his mind was not very clear.

His second statement was made after he had been told about the finding of the bones in the garden. He said that in the summer of 1943 he had been in the Police War Reserve, and his wife had been away in Sheffield. During her absence, he had met an Austrian girl in a snack bar, and she had come to visit him on two or three occasions. On the last time that she was there, a telegram was delivered announcing his wife's return. He had sexual intercourse with the girl on the bed, and in the course of this strangled her with a piece of rope and after this he had carried her naked body into the front room and after wrapping it up had put it under the floorboards. After his wife had returned that evening, he had waited until she left the house and had then moved the body of Fuerst to the wash-house, later burying it in the garden on the right-hand side near the rockery. He had later burned the clothing in an old dustbin which he had used as an incinerator. Some months later, while digging in the garden, he had accidentally unearthed her skull and had put it in the same dustbin.

It was in the same year that he met Nurse Muriel Eady, while he was working at Park Royal. He had taken her and her friend to Rillington Place and introduced them to his wife; they had been to tea on several occasions. She had complained of catarrh[1] and he arranged to see her while his wife was out, as he thought he could help her. He made her inhale a mixture of Friars Balsam from a square glass jar, which he had attached to the gas tap so as to force the coal through the liquid, with the idea of making her sleepy. She had become unconscious, and he had a vague recollection of tying a stocking around her neck and having intercourse with her at the same time.

He admitted that he was confused about this, and thought that this might have been the Austrian girl. In any event he had then buried her body in the garden.

In the next case, he said that he had met the girl in a café in February. She was with another girl, and he told them that he was shortly leaving his flat and suggested they should call during the evening. Only one of them came, and after agreeing to take the flat, subject to the landlord's permission, she suggested that she should stay with him for a few days. Once again, he asserted that there had been an argument and that the girl had threatened him. A fight had resulted; but he gave no more details, merely saying that she was on the floor, and that he must have put her in the cupboard immediately.

Finally he described how he had met his last victim with a man emerging from a café in Hammersmith. In this case he offered to put them both up for a few days, and they came to stay with him. There had been arguments, and both of them had left; but the girl had come back alone to ask him if her friend had called. When Christie had told her that he had not seen him she had replied that she would wait for him. Although he told her not to wait and she had insisted and this had lead to a struggle during

---

[1] The pathologist who examined the skull had noted symptoms of catarrh.

which her clothing was torn. Suddenly she went limp,[1] and he thought that her clothing must have become caught round her neck during the struggle. He said he tried to lift her and pulled her into the kitchen, and finding that her pulse had stopped and she was not breathing he opened the cupboard and put her inside. Again, he did not mention intercourse or gas.

After this, he had remained in the house for another three weeks, and when he had left, after spending three days in a Rowton House, he had wandered about until he had given himself up.

This story is fairly typical of this type of murderer who, because he has been discovered admits the basic essentials, but tends to colour them, black though they may be, in as nice a light as possible to make it all look rather less unpleasant, which in ways represents the next stage to avoiding being found out, that is to say to making it look as nice as possible. From the point of view of the investigating officer (and possibly the conscience of the criminal) this is excellent; a confession has been obtained and an arrest has been made whilst the accused feels not quite so bad as he might have done. From the point of view of the scientist it is most unsatisfactory because he has no accurate proof of his conclusions for future reference. In the Birmingham Y.W.C.A. murder, for example, a man named Byrne was arrested, tried and convicted. Everybody was satisfied; but in his statement he said he picked up a table knife in the room and cut off the girl's head. Every test applied to the knife and similar knives showed they could not do it. The admission was there but it was incorrect; quite clearly the accused man, whereas prepared to admit to the crime, did not want to admit that he took a knife specially to do it, and so long as he said he did it, nobody could care less. With the new homicide act, somebody will have to decide what to do

---

[1] In many strangulation cases this appears in the statement.

with the person convicted of murder. It is very relevant in such a case whether the convicted man took a knife with him or whether he just picked it up because it was there. Here the scientists need the most accurate information available so that they can present the alternatives as clearly as possible.

4 Pseudo-Science: The Coventry Case

The Christie case was an example of the success of scientific methods; the Coventry case was its exact opposite, demonstrating, albeit twenty-five years ago, the failure of scientific methods because of pseudo-science. Christie's activities were brought to light in sensational fashion and, from the outset, it was obvious that it was a major murder case; the case of Pamela Coventry was nothing more, initially, than the failure of a schoolgirl to return home. It was therefore treated as a much more routine matter and even at the height of investigations only one major expert, Sir Bernard Spilsbury, was called in to make his usual meticulous (but, as it proved on this occasion, incomplete) examination.

It was early in the spring term of 1939 that Pamela Coventry, a Hornchurch schoolgirl, set out after lunch from her home. She was to have met some friends at the end of the next road and to have gone on with them to dancing-class, for which she carried her dancing shoes in a brown paper bag. A shy girl, eleven years old, she did not speak readily to strangers, although, as it transpired later, she had struck up an acquaintance with a man in Coronation Drive – the street down which she walked on her way to school – a fortnight or so before, without her mother's knowledge.

Her friends had waited for her until 1.30 and then, assuming she had been delayed at home for some reason, went on without her. When she failed to return home on the night of 18th January, her mother raised the alarm and a police search was started. It was, however, a chance passer-by who found the body the next morning, on the local aerodrome. She had been stripped of clothing, except for her petticoat which was round her neck, and she had been trussed by tying her legs against her chest with electric flex and string.

Since it seemed unlikely that a murderer would be so careless as to dispose of the body locally, and as the scene of the crime adjoined the Metropolitan Police area, the first hypothesis was that the crime had been committed in London and the body returned to Hornchurch as a blind. The Chief Constable properly called in New Scotland Yard. Sir Bernard Spilsbury was asked to examine the body, which yielded more tangible information. There was, as expected, evidence of sexual assault but death had been caused by manual strangulation. From the stomach contents the pathologist firmly fixed the time of the murder to within an hour of the victim's last meal and concluded that death must have taken place between 1.20 and 1.45 p.m. and hence, by this evidence, in all probability in or near Coronation Drive itself.

The method by which the body had been tied suggested the most promising leads for two pieces of electric flex and some tarred garden string had been used. One of the former proved to be a very unusual 600 ohm, 7-strand type which had not been manufactured for seven years, whilst a green cable and the string – which were also used – were commonplace. In addition, at the autopsy, when the body was untied, there was a cigarette-butt, of the home-rolled variety, caught up between her thigh and abdomen. Subsequently, on 21st January, the girl's shoes were found in the paper bag she had been carrying, at a nearby spot which had been thoroughly searched two days before and which lent substance to the view of the investigating officers that a local man was responsible. Some time later buttons, a school badge and flex similar to that on the body were found wrapped in a *News Chronicle* for 11th January. It may well be significant that the flex was found shortly after a description of it was relayed to the Press by the police and published with a photograph.

Armed with this evidence, the Scotland Yard investigating officers assisted by the local police renewed their inquiries in the neighbourhood and within a few days had found a suspect, a man named Richardson, who lived in Coronation Drive. He had been living by himself at the time of the murder, as his wife was away in hospital, expecting a child; it was this that first drew attention to him, since both previous and subsequent experience has shown that sexual offences are frequently connected with the wife's absence or pregnancy. When interviewed, he claimed to have been elsewhere at the time designated by the pathologist but gave a somewhat incoherent story, although he stated emphatically that he had been at his sister-in-law's house at 1.30 and at work at his usual time. This was corroborated by his sister-in-law and by his employer. Other witnesses claimed to have seen him at his house at 1.15 whilst a milkman said that he had seen his kitchen light on at 5.20 a.m. the following morning. When asked to explain this, he said that he was trying to redecorate it in time for his wife's return. During the course of the interview, he was seen to roll and smoke a cigarette which appeared similar to that recovered from the dead girl's body.

His house was searched but no other evidence was disclosed except some green flex and string of the same type found on the body, together with a series of *News Chronicles* from which the issue for 11th January was missing. A mackintosh found in the house showed slight traces of human blood on the inside of the sleeve and pocket. It was also noted that the wire of the fence at the end of the garden, which adjoined the aerodrome, had been pressed down.

The prosecution's case, as presented at the committal proceedings, at Romford Magistrates' Court, therefore rested entirely upon the circumstantial and scientific evidence, for Richardson had not made the vestige of an admission. The first part of this evidence was the geographical proximity of Richardson and, to some extent, the time of death, and his alibi; the second part was as follows:

The electric flex: Evidence was called from Dr Roche Lynch, Home Office analyst, to say that the *green* sample from the body was similar to that found in Richardson's house. There was also some insulating tape.

The string: Similar evidence was given by the same expert.

The bloodstains found on the mackintosh were also stated by Dr Roche Lynch to be human blood but the group was said to be indeterminable and he estimated the age as being between two weeks and several months.

The cigarette-butt: An expert from the Imperial Tobacco Company stated that the cigarette-butt was identical to that taken from the accused during interrogation, in paper, tobacco and method of rolling.

The wire fence: Evidence was produced to show that this had been pressed down, clearly suggesting that this had been done whilst carrying the body over it.

The time of death: This was deduced from the state of digestion of the stomach contents.

Richardson was committed for trial at the Central Criminal Court on this evidence, where he was defended by Mr Winn (now Lord Justice Winn) who had represented him before the magistrate. This tactical policy might be worthy of further consideration by the legal profession because there was no doubt that all the prosecution witnesses, having been cross-examined by him in a tactful and pleasant manner at the lower court, when meeting him again amongst strangers regarded him as an 'old friend'. On this occasion, the defendant's solicitors had certainly not only done their homework properly but had briefed counsel accordingly. As a result the prosecution's evidence, which sounded so impressive at the committal and in the newspapers, was almost unrecognisable after cross-examination at the trial – questioning which was not

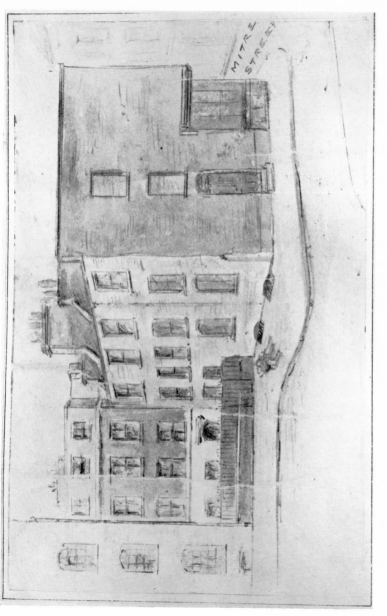

Sketch of Mitre Square immediately after the murder of Catherine Eddowes showing the body in position. Courtesy of the London Hospital

A post-mortem room in use five years ago. Courtesy of *Medicine
Science and the Law*

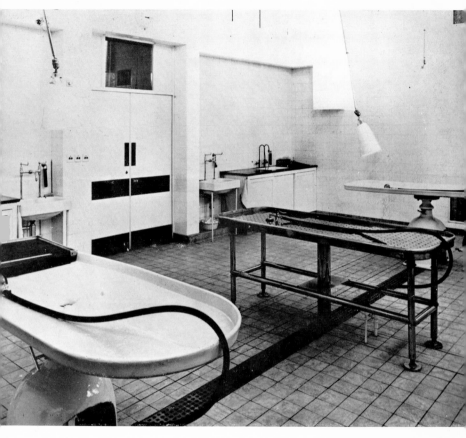

A modern post-mortem room, showing close similarity to an operating theatre. Courtesy of *Medicine Science and the Law*

John Christie (*by Philip Youngman-Carter*)
(see Appendix 1)

limited to defending counsel but also derived from the judge.

Again to take the main points as already outlined :

The green flex and string: It was pointed out that both were in common use and the judge in fact asked Dr Roche Lynch why it was deemed necessary to call an eminent analyst to give evidence on such matters as electrical flex and tape, which were obviously matters for experts from the manufacturing industry.

The bloodstains on the mackintosh: Dr Roche Lynch having said that from the distribution this could not have been due to a hand injury, it was indicated to him that that was an inference which should be drawn by the jury. At the same time it became obvious that the really relevant information as to whether it was the same blood group as the dead child was not to be forthcoming. This was simply explained because the blood group of the dead child was not known as Sir Bernard Spilsbury, at the autopsy, had omitted to take a blood sample. This omission was possibly assisted by his somewhat unapproachable manner, due no doubt to shyness, which prevented any of those present from drawing the attention of such an important expert to his failure.

The cigarette-butt: It transpired that the method by which similarity between samples of tobacco was established by experts in the tobacco trade in those days was by its 'smell after ignition'. This, of course, meant destruction of the sample. It is certain that now a closer approximation of two samples could be obtained by scientific methods which could include neutron activation. In addition, the same expert also gave evidence on the paper and method of rolling. Now the defence, seeking for expert opinions on tobacco, had been unable to find anyone willing to assist but did find an expert on cigarette-paper who proved to be one of the largest manufacturers and who showed no inhibition. His evidence was a perfect example of *not* accepting the obvious for, whereas the tobacco expert had said that the papers of the two samples were similar and had come from the same piece of paper, he – and he made them – said that any chance of getting similar matching between papers from the same packet was impossible for the method of cutting up the paper ensured this. In addition, the defence had taken the trouble to collect random samples of cigarette-butts from the factory floor and proved that they too showed the same 'similarity'.

The bent wire fencing was a similar example of evidence which sounds impressive but is misleading. The defence, who had taken the trouble to measure the height of the wire on the other two sides of the garden, found them, in fact, to be bent even more.

Finally, the time of death, based on undigested food in the stomach naturally remained unchallenged, although had it been desirable for the defence to do so, it could have shown that this observation is notoriously misleading as a stomach full of undigested food has on occasions been found more than twenty-four hours after a meal.

It was not, therefore, surprising that, although defence Counsel made a submission that the prosecution had not proved its case and the Judge ruled that this must be a decision for the jury, after hearing the evidence that the cigarette could have been rolled by hundreds of other people, the jury said that there was insufficient evidence to convict and found the prisoner not guilty.

This case has been chosen deliberately because, although it took place twenty-five years ago when forensic science was less advanced than at the present day, it does nevertheless illustrate, by hindsight, some of the situations which it is the object of this book to overcome. First, co-operation between the C.I.D. of New Scotland Yard and the County Forces is now much closer and even more integration has been achieved by regional crime squads; at the time of the Pamela Coventry murder there was undoubtedly some feeling that the local crime investigation department who had more knowledge of local conditions should have been more closely consulted. Admittedly on this occasion there may have been some clash of personalities but co-operation between the two Forces involved could not have been better than in the case of Stanley Setty (1959) which in fact involved the body of a man killed in London and dumped in the Essex Marshes by aeroplane.

Secondly, and far the most important lesson, was the danger of relying upon experts and *not what they know.* Thus, had the assistance of experts in the special problems been enlisted, not only would there have been no comments from the Judge but the relative probability of the accuracy of the comparisons would have been appreciated. Apparently the legal profession does not always appreciate the fact that experts are limited in their expertise and that 'big names', although they may carry weight in court, do not necessarily stand up to cross-examination outside their own subjects, even if experienced as witnesses. A somewhat comparable situation arose in *The Well of Loneliness* case, when an eminent toxicologist was called to give evidence as to whether certain passages referring to lesbianism were obscene.

Finally, there was the failure to collect blood for grouping at the autopsy, an omission which although academically unforgivable could still occur in the absence of team-work and properly trained personnel working in harmony with the pathologist and able to point out his omissions.

A final comment would appear to be justified. It was most interesting to note that while Dr Roche Lynch was rebuked for saying that the bloodstains on the mackintosh could not have come from a hand injury, yet Sir Bernard Spilsbury was allowed to put forward in most emphatic terms a theory that the same stains came from the nostril of the dead girl as she took her last breath. This may be said to indicate that an expert's reputation may impress the court rather than what he says and suggests that proof of expertise is essential in each case. In any event, in this case the jury were not impressed but there still remains some lingering doubt as to whether, if the defence had not been so alert and efficient, on the basis of the evidence produced a miscarriage of justice might not have occurred.

When considering the case of Pamela Coventry in retrospect, two thoughts enter the mind and must always be the subject of the reappraisal following an acquittal in any criminal case. The first, of course, is what sort of reasoning went on in the minds of the jury. It is to be suspected that, in spite of any prejudice which may have resulted from the publication of the evidence for the prosecution at the Magistrates' Court, the weakness of the points that were made was enhanced by the failure to produce evidence of the matters which would have been of greater significance. Thus there was not any link between the *unusual* piece of flex and the accused; furthermore, the murderer clearly knew of its significance and discarded it. Then there was the anticlimax of the 'bent down' wire and the method of manufacture of the cigarette papers. Yet, had the defence not conducted its own investigation, both, unchallenged, might have been very damaging.

However, the really vital point in the case was the blood on Richardson's sleeve and, whereas at the present day, with the advent of the Coombs-Dodd test, the problem of too small a quantity to group would not arise, it would nevertheless have been of little use to have known the group of the bloodstain because the blood group of the dead girl was not known. It is easy, so long as members of the legal profession in England have no training in forensic science, for a false appraisal of the real significance of scientific evidence to occur. Unless critically challenged such evidence may have a greater impact on the jury than it deserves. This is no fault of the scientists but examples have occurred, even in recent years. For example, it sounds scientifically impressive, and jurors and courts always pay great attention to science, when evidence is given that mud on a tyre is similar to that at the scene of a crime. Yet when it can be shown that it is also similar to that of numerous other places in the vicinity, on a purely scientific basis it has no significance at all. Then the mere comparison of two fibres by colour and character is not sufficient scientifically unless it can be shown that the dye used is similar; a single fibre may be of minor importance compared with several. Sometimes great importance is laid on trivialities such as the difference of half an inch in the height of a body compared with the alleged known height of the missing person though all sorts of factors may play a part, including the height of the heels of the shoes. It is for this reason that a single common feature may be of little significance whilst if there are four or five, possibility becomes probability.

Finally, all scientific evidence, especially when technical methods are used, must be subjected to the most careful scrutiny before being submitted to the court. For example, in the use of photographs the technique may demand reduction or enlargement of the objects to be compared, and it is therefore advisable to show the court that a proper comparison has been made and, if possible, with what result.

Time and time again the scientific expert is faced with the problem of assessing the true evidential value of some observation, and may even be pressed to include it in his evidence. Unless fully satisfied that it will stand up to true scientific standards, he should discard it as evidence. Clearly, however, all observation should be included in a report to be viewed by other experts but to include matters of doubtful scientific significance may possibly be prejudicial. Either it means something and this should be said, or it does not, in which case it should not be mentioned.

5 Original Methods: George Joseph Smith and Emmett-Dunne

The repetitive murder is no rarity in the annals of crime and in the end its very success has proved to be the undoing of its operator. In the main this has been due to over-confidence which appears to develop a feeling of omnipotence whereby the very ingenuity and care, which were the basis of previous success, give way to behaviour which, unless blessed with unbelievable luck, must end in suspicion. This will inevitably, when the past is scrutinized, lead to detection. Most examples of this kind are motivated by financial gain. One of the best examples was that of George Haigh who, by being orthodox and selecting those who, having no roots, would not be missed, and by liquidating the whole family unit and thereby being able to collect all the assets, evolved an almost foolproof technique so long as he maintained his caution. At the same time he gave himself additional security through the original idea of completely destroying the bodies of his victims with acid. His downfall came when he chose Mrs Durand Deakin, a rich widow living in a Kensington hotel with habits so regular that her absence would be bound to cause comment. As though this were not enough he also sold her fur coat and jewellery in such a way and in such a place that it was bound to be identified and linked up with himself. Under such circumstances no amount of luck could help him and he was reduced to a not very credible defence of insanity.

In the same way, had George Joseph Smith restricted himself to one murder by his own ingenious method it can be safely claimed that he would never have been detected, even if suspected, by any post-mortem examination findings. But after eight repeats of the same type of bigamy and three murders by the same method all with a similar background had aroused suspicion he was inevitably in jeopardy when the circumstances of the several deaths were compared. Even then it was only the observance of the father of one of his victims that brought him under suspicion. This was not because he was a skilled or cunning worker, for he not only used his own name on several occasions but very rarely concealed his interest in the financial worth of his brides, but because communication was poor at the time and his method of killing was original.

Smith first came to the attention of the police at the age of nineteen, when he was convicted of larceny. Having served his six months imprisonment he emerged in 1891 to lead a roving life, in the course of which he claimed to have served in the Northamptonshire Regiment. By the end of 1894 he was in prison again for larceny, and although he married Caroline Beatrice Thornhill soon after his release, using the name of Love, he did not settle down to domestic bliss of the usual kind. Instead, within a year of his wedding, he went through a form of marriage with another woman in London, with an eye to possible blackmail and demands for money. Unfortunately, his other methods of obtaining ready cash earned him a further two-year sentence at Hastings early in 1901, and it was not until some five years after his release that he seems to have recovered sufficient confidence to resume his activities in this direction. Within the one month of July of 1908, he had defrauded one woman of about £80 under promise of marriage, and had bigamously married another. Strangely enough, he was genuinely fond of the latter, Edith Pegler, and developed the habit of returning to her at regular intervals after fleecing yet another gullible member of her sex. Within a year he had found his next victim, whom he deprived of £260 by 'marrying' her, this time under the name of Rose, obtaining her worldly wealth in cash, and then taking her to the National Gallery. Here he left her for a moment on the most natural of pretexts, never to reappear. His visits to the National Gallery were part of his adopted character for the purpose of these schemes, for he was in the habit of posing as an antique dealer and attributing his ill-gotten gains to fortunate 'finds' of rarities.

In his next attempt, however, Smith was not so lucky. A chance meeting at Clifton led him into complications which were eventually to lead him to the dock and gallows. It was in the summer of 1910 when he met the thirty-three-year-old daughter of a deceased bank manager, Beatrice Munday, who had fairly considerable private means. They were married at the registry office on 26th August, Smith using the name of Henry Williams. He soon found out that most of his bride's money was in the hands of trustees, who paid her the interest on £2,500 in monthly instalments. He did however manage to extract from them £138, with which he absconded on 13th September. He left an explanatory note accusing his 'wife' of giving him venereal disease – he had discovered that she had previously had a lover – and saying that he had gone to London for a cure. So far, all had gone well, even if the haul had not been as great as he had hoped. He spent the next four months moving round the country as a rather unsuccessful antique dealer, in the company of Edith Pegler. He had become restless again by March 1911 and his wanderings took him to Weston-super-Mare, and – something he can scarcely have intended – to Beatrice Munday, who was overjoyed to see him. She found him gazing out to sea on the front, and took him back to her lodgings; but her landlady took an instant dislike to him and they were on the move once again. By May, they had settled in Herne Bay, taking a house on a monthly lease; and it was here he put into execution a new plan by which he would be able to obtain all her resources. He accordingly took Counsel's opinion and made a will in her favour (having nothing) – in return for a similar provision on her part. This, if a somewhat one-sided bargain, appeared to her reasonable enough, but the sequence of events which followed suggested an ulterior motive far from innocent.

The wills having been executed on 8th July, Smith on the next day went and bought a cheap iron bath for the house. This was followed by a visit to Dr French, a local doctor, to whom he told the story that his wife had had a fit, and asked him to prescribe something for her. Dr French subsequently visited her and she denied having suffered from anything more than a headache. Two further visits by the doctor revealed nothing worse than lassitude, which could well have resulted from the bromide which he had originally prescribed. In spite of this she wrote to her uncle giving Smith's version of her illness and saying that she had had two bad fits. She also explained that she had made a will in his favour lest anything should happen to her.

On 13th July, Dr French in answer to a note from Smith, which said simply: 'Can you come at once? I am afraid my wife is dead', went round to the house and found Beatrice Munday lying on her back in the bath with her head beneath the water and a piece of soap grasped in her hand. Though he attempted to revive her, she was clearly dead. An inquest was held two days later, and Smith managed to impress the coroner sufficiently to persuade him to ignore the request of the family for a postmortem examination which had been received the day after the inquest. The only evidence given was that of Smith and Dr French, and nothing was heard of the recently made wills or of the purchase of the bath. Probate of the will had been granted by 11th September. The next summer (1912) he was back again with Edith Pegler and told her that his new found wealth came from the sale of a Chinese idol during a visit to Canada.

On this occasion Smith spent a year with the lady but resumed his independence in October 1913. Within a very short space of time, he had found yet another bride, Alice Burnham, when he induced her to marry him within a few days of meeting her at Southsea. The only delay in carrying out the ceremony was due to her parents' opposition, for her father took an instant and violent dislike to Smith, which resulted in a visit to her home being cut short by his objections to Smith's behaviour. All the same the wedding took place on 4th November by which time Smith had proposed an insurance of her life for £500 (3rd November). By 29th November despite Mr Burnham's continued suspicion he had been induced to part with £100 belonging to Alice. On 4th December Smith completed the insurance on Alice Burnham's life which was followed by her signing a will in his favour on 8th December. Within three days she had died in Blackpool in a similar way to Beatrice Munday. The inquest which produced the same verdict, included evidence, in some detail, of a faint or fit which on this occasion was attributed to a 'heart disease'.

Once more Smith, following his usual pattern, returned to his wanderings with Edith Pegler, and on this occasion stayed with her until just after the beginning of the first world war. His next 'wife' was rather more fortunate, for she only lost her life savings, and did not become the subject of an inquest. She was a domestic servant, Alice Reavil, whom Smith married on 17th September and absconded with her money five days later. Once again he returned to Edith to whom he gave some of Alice's clothing.

The interval between marrying Alice Reavil and taking his next bride was even briefer; for Smith's boldness was clearly increasing with each success. By 17th December he had married Alice Lofty, a lady whose lack of private means he remedied by insuring her life. On this occasion he signed the register using the name of John

Lloyd and on the same day escorted his bride from Bath to London to rooms which he had booked in Highgate the previous Monday after asking to see the bath. However, he proved to have made such a bad impression on the landlady that when they arrived she refused them entry, and they had to go to lodgings which Smith found nearby. The following day Alice Lofty was found dead in her bath. The inquest held on 1st January, 1915, went just as smoothly as before and a verdict of 'suffocation by drowning in the water' was returned.

On this occasion Smith's luck had at long last run out. Charles Burnham, his father-in-law several times removed, happened to notice the newspaper report of the inquest on Alice Lofty and forwarded it to the Aylesbury police, whilst a Mr Crossley, the landlord of the house where Alice Burnham had succumbed, sent a copy together with a cutting on the Burnham inquest to the Blackpool police. After this it was not long before Smith was arrested on charges of making false declarations in the marriage register at Bath, and on 23rd March he was first charged with the murders of his three bigamous wives. This had followed a full investigation by the police into Smith's aliases and financial affairs, which had revealed the extraordinary extent of his activities. However, the Herne Bay episode concerning Beatrice Munday only became known on 15th February.

The trial opened on 22nd June, 1915 at the Central Criminal Court before Mr Justice Scrutton, and the evidence outlined the story as already related. The main problem which faced the prosecution was to prove that the deaths were due to deliberate murder and not a series of coincidences. This task fell to the lot of Sir Bernard Spilsbury, and his evidence established a very strong case. He had carried out experiments to show that if the legs of a person lying in a bath were suddenly jerked upwards, the resultant immersion of the head could result in vagal inhibition due to the water suddenly impinging on the back of the throat, or drowning from posture and immobility. In fact he nearly killed a policeman's daughter who had volunteered to act as a guinea pig. Even he, however, had to admit the possibility of coincidence and accident. The case largely rested on the evidence of system; and this Marshall Hall, K.C. for the defence, was unable to destroy. His closing speech was remarkable for its brevity in a trial of such importance, but it only took the jury twenty-two minutes to find Smith guilty. His appeal was dismissed and he was duly executed.

Smith had successfully committed bigamy eight times, and murder three times, before he was caught through his own stupidity. It is a remarkable record; yet the bigamy offences could probably be repeated today without too much difficulty. A bigamist who chooses to use his own name can produce an absolutely genuine birth certificate with no markings to indicate whether he is already married, and even that is not yet required by law. Even the murders, provided they were not connected with one another, could also still remain undetected if unsuspected. One way in which suspicion might nowadays be aroused is from the routine inquiry as to life insurance which the Coroner's officer must make; but even then there is nothing to prevent the man giving an incorrect answer. That death can occur from sudden immersion is now well recognised and the Brides in the Bath case has created in the minds of those who have been trained in forensic medicine a strongly suspicious attitude to anyone who dies in a bath or bathroom. Nevertheless in death due to cardial arrest the post-mortem findings are entirely based on negative factors, the most important being lack of any signs of drowning and lack of any cause for fainting or loss of consciousness. It is also possible that the gripping of the legs might leave traceable bruising.

Although from the historical and sensational point of view it is from the repetitive aspect that the case has achieved fame. From the medicolegal aspect its importance lies in the demonstration of a new method of murder which owing to lack of signs of violence and negative findings at the autopsy could deceive the unwary or unsuspicious. The real clue to the situation and the possibility of homicide was arrived at when the fact *that the method had been repeated* and motive and cause were taken as a whole. If there were to be established a central registry of cause of unexpected deaths classified under headings such as *'in bath'*, it would lead to cases geographically far apart being shown to have identical causation and bring many such coincidences to light.

Anything which smacks too strongly of a police state such as a personal identity card is regarded with abhorrence by the British public; yet the choice is more one between the safety of their persons and property and the sacrifice of one or two very minor details of privacy. There are many crimes which would be made considerably harder, though it is idle to claim that they would be entirely prevented, by the use of personal registration cards, giving details of the bearer's personal standing, age, and fingerprints.[1] Once it was understood that to have to produce these was not an affront to personal dignity, but a necessary part of the administration of law and order, they would be no more of a burden than a driving licence. Yet there is no sign of any attempt to begin work on these lines, for which the future George Joseph Smiths of this world are doubtless duly thankful.

Smith succeeded for two reasons; but the reasons for his failure were over-confidence and stupidity. The reasons for his success were, in addition to those already discussed, the originality of his method and the difficulty in proof of a cause of death. In fact it can be reiterated that, without three similar types of death, no cause might ever either have come to light or have been proved by experiment.

[1] Proposals for a national fingerprint record are now under consideration by the Home Office.

In 1953 a somewhat similar case occurred which was not revealed by repetition, but by local suspicion. This was maintained after the death, but was precipitated by a single act – marriage.

The reason for describing the case is that it seems incredible that when thousands of men were trained to kill by unarmed combat during the war, no cases have been described since the end of the war except this particular incident. The story when reduced to basic facts is simple. Sergeant Walters of R.E.M.E. had the distinction of being one of the few men of whom nobody could say a bad word in the whole course of an investigation on him. He was married to an attractive German girl. A friend of the family was a Sergeant Emmett-Dunne – tall, handsome and with a fine record for gallantry. On 30th November at 11 p.m. Mrs Walters rang the sergeants' mess to ask about her husband who had not returned home. A search took place led by Emmett-Dunne and was repeated at about 3 a.m., when Walters was found hanging from the balustrade of the training block. Help was summoned and the body was eventually taken to the Military Hospital at Hostert where a very careful autopsy was performed by an inexperienced though very painstaking Army pathologist who found that death was due to hanging, and a court of enquiry recorded death as being due to suicide. And so the matter rested, although none of the German drivers of whom Walters was in charge would believe that he had killed himself. The following year Emmett-Dunne married Mrs Walters. It was this that triggered off an explosion of rumours which resulted in Colonel Frank Elliott of the S.I.B., who had been absent when Walters died, re-examining the original file. He then was puzzled to find that the pathologist had found a fracture of the thyroid cartilage (Adam's apple) in the mid line, an injury of which he had not heard before. The Army authorities decided to reopen the case and requested the help of the C.I.D., and New Scotland Yard; and Superintendent

Colin MacDougal was put on the case. After preliminary investigations it was considered that there was sufficient evidence to justify exhuming the body of Walters from Cologne Military Cemetery. This was done on 26th February and as a result the findings (fractured larynx) of the pathologist were confirmed. Now this type of injury is extremely rare but it was possible by experiment to show the mechanism by which it could be produced. This was by a blow with a linear object across the front of the neck (not as in ju jitsu across the side). The sort of object which could produce it was a round wooden ruler but it was found that there would be visible external marks. It therefore seemed that it must have been caused by a smooth pliable object and the obvious solution appeared to be the edge of a hand which is used in unarmed combat. The instructor who had taught Emmett-Dunne confirmed the technique.

This also explained the fact that apart from the marks of the cord there was nothing to show that death resulted from hanging or that Walters was alive when hanged. As a result of a brilliant example of methodical investigation by Superintendent Colin MacDougal, Emmett-Dunne was convicted of murder by a general court martial at Düsseldorf. The interest of the case lies in the nearly successful attempt to disguise murder as suicide (which gives reason for thought as to how many have succeeded) and in the method used. Many men must have been taught unarmed combat. If none of these men have used their knowledge since, it speaks well for their self-control; but even if they have, their victim's death is all too likely to have been recorded as from natural causes. Concealed homicide is a type of crime which can only be detected where there is suspicion; and, as Smith and Emmett-Dunne have shown, poisoning is not the only means that must be looked for once such suspicion has been aroused.

PART TWO

6 The Past and the Present: The Problem of Integration

The picture that has been built up in the first part of this story of the past and present is hardly encouraging for the future security of the honest citizen or for the police, especially when the ratio of incidence of crime to its detection is examined. In Radzinowicz's words: 'It is the calculated risk that matters to the intelligent criminal and, at the moment, everything shows that that risk is well worth taking.' In homicide, the investigator and his assistants have in the past been at a grave disadvantage, because of lack of training or knowledge, combined with lack of organisation. The criminal is essentially an independent operator; against him must be ranged the only specific reply: a highly organised, well integrated, scientifically trained force for maintaining order. The criminal, however, dare not create too large an organisation, as the Great Train Robbery has taught the rank-and-file. While his lawful opponents can afford to do this they, in their turn, must be doubly alert to failures of co-ordination. The ability to organise can well be regarded as their trump-card but, at the moment, there is no doubt that they are not putting it to full use. There are too few critical examinations of the system and attempts to prevent lapses; only when defects are shown up in practice are they remedied.

Organisation: The Multiple Authorities

This is particularly true of forensic science itself. It is hoped that attention may be drawn to potential weaknesses as we proceed but this is the first and most obvious of them. At the moment, the simplest example is the curious division of forensic science which divorces the so-called forensic pathologists' laboratories from other clinical and scientific activities. It is not unique to this country, for it is to be found in the United States as well; and despite brilliant individual efforts in all fields, it tends to lead to superficial co-operation and not to real integration of energy, as it is bound to foster jealousy. In no forensic science laboratory in England is there a fully qualified pathologist or police surgeon working on the spot. On the other hand there is always present a serving police officer for liaison purposes. Thus, the scientist who is always in close contact with the police, is in a position to discuss in his own environment possible lines of approach or to explain the significance of the findings in cases such as safe-breaking or burglary. The medicolegal experts, pathologists and police surgeons who are dealing with similar problems of crimes of violence, have little opportunity for consultation with either the investigating officers or the scientists, other than at the scene of the crime, at the examination of the victim, or when meetings are specially arranged. In fact, it has been said that the pathologist may see the investigating officer only at the autopsy and the trial.

There is also an arbitrary division of material between the forensic and pathological laboratories. Hair, blood, and clothing are examined by the scientist whilst the body and the wounds are the perquisites of the pathologist. The situation is further complicated by the independent control of the body by the Coroner, who is responsible for the choice of pathologist, subject only to consultation with the Chief of Police.[1] As he is administrative director of investigation into the cause of death, the consent of the Coroner must be obtained before a medico-jurist can

[1] Coroners' Rules – 1953.

92

examine a body (once dead) at the scene of the crime – a situation which, to some extent, involves the question of payment. He has, however, no control over any public mortuary or its staff, for these are under the local authority. He can only direct where a body be removed, but if no mortuary-keeper is available he cannot insist on its admission, nor can he, other than by diplomacy, improve on the working conditions therein.

Even by the slow standards to which modern organisational evolution has accustomed us, the whole situation is one of multiplied controls which have become increasingly involved. This, in spite of years of complaints which date back to 1888, is truly an example of the petty authority of the small local unit overriding the interests of the whole. But before discussing the causes we must look at the overall picture today, leaving the implications to speak for themselves. At the same time it will rapidly become clear that any future solution must involve seeking the co-operation and understanding of the public by a greater interchange of ideas. Without this any new organisation that may emerge may well be paralysed by a similar lack of elasticity. Much can be learnt from the experience of some laboratories (not by any means limited to the forensic sphere) where a combination of lack of vision at a higher level, with the inevitable lack of funds and staff, has led to levelling down to a mediocre standard, apathy towards research and repression of initiative.

Finance

The first matter for comment concerns the method of financing a case. Basically there are two main branches of any police force: the uniformed branch, which is in charge of law enforcement and prevention of crime, and the criminal investigation department, which is in charge of detection. There is quite a definite dividing line between these two, although the uniform branch plays some essential part in most criminal investigations. Such a situation

is particularly interesting when the statement of Radzino-
wicz, that the best form of prevention is detection, is
accepted. Both branches are financed by the local authority
with a grant from the Home Office, except in the case of
the Metropolitan Police, who enjoy a special status.
Furthermore, the latter's officers may be called in on cases
outside their area, when they may be paid from the local
force's funds, depending on circumstances and the stage
at which their help is required.

There is a curious mixture of whole-time salaries and
part-time payments with statutory expenses. The sources
are themselves varied, not only in origin but in the manner
of their disbursement. All C.I.D. officers, for example, are
recruited from the uniformed branch and continue to be
paid from that same source, although their training and
organisation are entirely different. So too are their outlook,
their free time and their life – both at home and at work.
Then there is the Coroner's officer, of whom much more
will be heard later. He is the investigating officer into all
unexpected or unnatural deaths. Whilst he assists the
Coroner, he is still attached to the local police station and
is a member of the uniform branch. Yet, although an investigating officer, and perhaps the key officer in the suspicion of homicide, he has no systematic training in forensic
science or investigation, his knowledge having been
acquired traditionally, 'picked-up', by acting as deputy to
his predecessor. In county forces it is usually the practice
for the officer whose case it is to act as coroner's officer
and he in fact does not even benefit from his predecessor's
knowledge.

The forensic science laboratories outside the Metropolitan area are financed from the Home Office on a
capitation basis of the police forces which use their services,
although police officers attached to them as liaison officers
are paid by the police. They are equipped likewise on a
Home Office budget. The salaries, which are far from com-
petitive with those paid by industry, are on fixed scales.

The central local authorities[1] pay for the coroners, jury and witnesses (including pathologists), and the cost of removal of the bodies. The last two expenses are authorised by the coroner as also are special fees such as for toxicological examination. The university departments are supported through the University Grants Committee, and the latter finances the salaries and equipment of those who work in them – pathologists, serologists and chemists. The regular employment of other pathologists is within the National Health Service in hospital laboratories. In the event of a criminal prosecution, the fees for attendance at court and preparation of the case (qualifying fee) are paid by the court and originate from the central local authority, while the defence fees may be provided by the Law Society under legal aid (prior to committal) and by the court afterwards.

The fees of expert witnesses are statutory, as also are travelling expenses; and the result, in terms of reward for very expert service, is only moderate and somewhat anomalous, to say the least. The fees paid by Coroners for medical witnesses are also statutory : five guineas for each post-mortem examination and three guineas for attendance and giving evidence at each inquest even if the latter involves more than one body. There is also a small mileage allowance. Fees for special examinations are laid down on schedule by the central local authority; the Coroner may obtain sanction to pay extra in special cases. It is of interest that in the event of the police authority paying for the services of a pathologist, a proportion is reclaimed from the Home Office, whilst if the Coroner pays, the whole expense falls upon the ratepayers. This fact has not escaped the notice of certain authorities. The fees paid to medical experts, as medicolegal fees do not fall within the terms of service of the National Health Service, may be retained by its employees. In the case of members of University

[1] These are the County Council, City or County Borough Authorities.

Staff and Civil Servants who are under contract, fees may be payable to the employer. Until a short time ago all such fees were paid on behalf of the Coroner by his officer in each case and against a signed receipt, the Coroner being reimbursed by the central local authority. Recently the new Greater London Council has decided to pay direct by cheque. Finally, there are a small group of unattached experts who are remunerated in the same way and personally retain their fees and provide their own services.

The local authority[1] is also responsible for the mortuaries and post-mortem rooms as well as the salaries of those who work in them. In the past the mortuary attendants' duties were limited to the care of the premises and admission and discharge of the bodies. This did not require any special skill or qualifications and not surprisingly was paid on a low scale. In some cases, residential accommodation was included in return for special responsibilities. Neither the Coroner, the police nor the pathologist has administrative control over the mortuary building or staff, since this remains in the hands of the local authority financing them. In many areas outside the large cities, the local authority, with the consent of the Coroner, has arranged with the hospital to share mortuary facilities; but this has to be the result of co-operation which is not always forthcoming from either party. In any event, hospital mortuary attendants receive, in addition to a salary, a small sum from the hospital for each post-mortem. There is no recognised training for this work.

The complications of the financing arrangements and the administrative aspect are closely related, having evolved together in a piecemeal fashion as a result of political and emotional pressures both from within and without. Changes have not taken into consideration the broader picture of social, medical and scientific advances and in particular the impact of World War II with an almost

[1] These are Borough, Urban or Rural District Councils.

unprecedented increase in crime, both qualitative and quantitative.

Part of the machinery for the investigation of homicide has already been mentioned; and this should have given an indication of the lack of a truly central co-ordinated administration which has resulted from the haphazard establishment and financing of a number of different small units. Each of these is subject to all the influences which go hand-in-hand with such situations – lack of interest, lack of knowledge, lack of publicity, lack of finance, lack of ambition combined with too much fear of authority or of unpopularity in high quarters.

Mortuaries

The best example of the well-recognised pattern is the situation presented by the public mortuaries. It is proposed to use them as an example, for it is within their walls that the early, and often the most vital stages, of the investigation of homicide take place. It was in such a context that Sir Bernard Spilsbury failed to collect the blood of the victim in the Pamela Coventry case. Before describing this example of social, political and administrative 'sweeping under carpets', the reader is referred to Figure ii which shows the public mortuary in one of the large cities which was in use for Coroners' autopsies five years ago. When studying this post-mortem room, it is as well to bear in mind that the incidence of tuberculosis amongst pathologists and mortuary attendants was, then, one of the highest in any occupation. Yet at the time of any post-mortem examination of the possible victim of homicide, those present may well (and should) include : one or more pathologists; a police surgeon; the chief investigating officer, together with the senior officer in charge of the case and his own assistant, a photographer and his assistant; an exhibit officer; a forensic scientist and one or two post-mortem assistants. Some pathologists make a practice of taking a secretary to make notes, and she also has to find somewhere to be able to write or type. There will also, of course, have to be room for the central figure itself and for real efficiency there should be space for laying out and packaging clothing, and for containers for collection of samples of blood, urine, stomach contents, hair and the like. To appreciate fully what this photograph really means, one must bear in mind that in addition to the conditions it shows, there will be a strong odour; the room is also gloomy. The attitude which perpetuates such conditions is exemplified by the reply of the Lord Mayor of Newcastle to a pathologist who gave the poor state of mortuaries as a reason for emigrating to Australia: 'What else do you expect in such places?' Now turn to Figure iii, which shows what can be achieved. This is one of three modern mortuaries in the central part of London, but unfortunately there are at least seven obsolete ones in existence, if not all in use. It is true that all have refrigerators, which is more than can be said of all hospitals; but none has a proper 24-hour service. However, the history of how this remarkable 'past' achievement has come to pass certainly offers cause for thought.

In 1888, during the activities of Jack the Ripper, the conditions of the mortuary and the mortuary attendant were commented upon by both doctors and Coroner (page 24). Admittedly the Coroner must have been a man who was not afraid to express his opinions, because later in the series the body was deliberately removed from his jurisdiction, to that of another Coroner who was more amenable. In 1926 Sir Bernard Spilsbury reiterated the same complaints, while in 1938, although men such as Dr Bullough, late County Medical Officer of Health for Essex, did achieve some results, most protests were equally unavailing. After the war, when building was at a standstill, it was not to be expected that much could be done, although there was no embargo on painting and decorating. It was only in 1953, as a result of evidence submitted to the Inter-Departmental Committee on Coroners, that official consideration was given to the situation, but owing to the terms of reference the report was limited to defining minimum requirements such as hot and cold running water, proper lights and heating. However a working party was subsequently set up by the Ministry of Town and Country Planning which in the course of its duties paid a visit to certain mortuaries. Those members of the party who had only heard descriptions, which they admitted later they did not believe, had a unique and rather shocking experience which resulted in a report being published by the Stationery Office containing the basic plans for a mortuary and post-mortem room.[1] The recommendations were only applicable to new mortuaries but did at least prevent local authorities from perpetuating the obsolete. In 1960 Sissons published a paper pleading yet again for improvement (in *Medicine, Science and the Law*). Finally, during the Committee stage of the Greater London Council Bill assurances were given by the Home Secretary that certain of the suggestions put forward by Lord Morrison would be given consideration, notably that the local authority should provide equipment and improved facilities, but at the same time he would not agree that the premises and staff should be the responsibility of the central authority who could then delegate to the Coroner. And there the matter still rests in London.

Now, when discussing problems associated with pathologists, an argument is always heard that conditions differ and that what may apply to London does not necessarily apply elsewhere. This may well be true but the statement (already quoted) by Dr Colin Corby, a forensic pathologist attached to the North East Forensic Science Laboratory, gave as one of the reasons for emigrating to Australia the unsatisfactory conditions of some of the mortuaries in the North of England. Although the future of this aspect

[1] This report has been included in *Jarvis on Coroners* (ninth edition).

of investigation will be discussed later, certain points must be mentioned here. Firstly in order to do skilled work, conditions must be good. Secondly, it is sometimes forgotten that whereas in certain people sensibility may be blunted by constant contact with dead bodies and brutality, and that details of such cases may also appeal to those who enjoy the sensational, there still exist some to whom this aspect of life (or death) has no aesthetic appeal. Amongst these are the police officers and others who have to enter post-mortem rooms when involved in investigational procedure. In the interests of efficiency there should be no need to add to this by unnecessarily bad working conditions which may even mean a risk of exposure to disease. A modern post-mortem room, properly maintained, need have no smell, no dust and can have adequate space. If conditions cannot be generally improved, or until they are, suitable mortuaries should be designated for criminal cases, and no others used.

The best indication of the persistence of bad conditions and practices is shown by what happens when an emergency involving somebody important has arisen. An excellent example of this was when a Member of Parliament was killed and his body was taken to a public mortuary. This resulted in the mortuary being cleaned and painted overnight. Public opinion still can exert influence; but as members of the Press have said, 'Who is interested in mortuaries?' The answer is simple : those who have to work in them and those who have to identify a dead person.

Although the surroundings matter, those who work in them and look after them are just as important. Thus a bad or old building can, in the hands of a man of administrative skill with high standards, be kept clean and, in fact, be better than a new building in the hands of an incompetent and dirty attendant. It follows that it is essential that those who are in charge should be properly selected. Unfortunately the position of mortuary superintendent is not autonomous and from tradition he appears to be subordinate to a Health Inspector. As such he is paid on a lower scale and, at the same time, this situation has never encouraged direct contact with his administrative head, the Medical Officer of Health. This has depressed initiative and fostered inactivity. Nor is the status accorded him a true indication of the responsibilities vested in the man, which require a high standard of both integrity and tact, the first in dealing with property, the second with relatives. From the medicolegal point of view it also requires a high degree of intelligence; for the preservation of clothing and other evidence is of paramount importance. The difference in standard between the hospital post-mortem room assistant in the academic atmosphere of a teaching hospital and that of an experienced (and there are very few of them) public mortuary superintendent is best appreciated by experience; on a number of occasions, the possible victim of homicide has been taken to a hospital, where the body has been undressed (and the clothing destroyed), washed (and vital evidence removed), and the orifices plugged (and evidence of rape lost). Such incidents are more numerous than is generally realised. One of the main difficulties has been to attract the right type of man, which is partly due to the fact that the work has been put forward as something disgusting, to be disliked, and not requiring any skill or interest. In addition no proper system of training has been developed : this could easily be established on the basis of apprenticeship.

Finally, due to the lack of proper centralisation, no really efficient 24-hour service has evolved. As a result, in a situation where several hours each day must be devoted to cleaning up to provide proper standards of cleanliness, if the staff are to keep reasonable hours, the time devoted to autopsies must be limited. This could be overcome by staggering the staff hours, which would also give the resident member proper time for leisure.

Next in importance after the provision of accommodation for the body is its removal and transport from the scene of death to the mortuary. This is mainly done by funeral directors or, in certain districts, by an ambulance. In the first case, where business interests must play a part and competition exists, it is the usual practice for the Coroner's officer to request the firm who will do the burial to move the body.

In London, there is one exception: the Jewish Burial Society, who do not usually wish to do the removal. The whole procedure has one grave disadvantage because it causes delay whilst finding out who is to do the removal and secondly because it may have to be fitted in with other funeral arrangements. These are however relatively unimportant from the medicolegal point of view compared with the handling of the body by those who are not trained in investigational procedure and are not restricted in outside communication.

7 The Organisation of a Present-Day Investigation

Some years ago a senior detective officer and his sergeant went from New Scotland Yard, at the request of a provincial force, to investigate a murder. On their arrival, they found certain omissions in the preliminary stages of the investigation. The sergeant started to make certain comments on this when his senior officer – a shrewd Scot – stopped him with the observation : 'We're here to detect, not criticise.' Perhaps such advice might be adopted more often under other circumstances. Certainly it is not the object of this book to criticise in any way the integrity, efficiency or organisation of the police force for, allowing for the shortage of personnel, it is remarkable what it has achieved. In fact, it should be stressed that, far from suggesting radical reforms of methods and organisation in that direction, any solution to the problems of the investigation and control of crimes of violence must be based upon the assumption that one of the failures lies in the inadequacy of the assistance of science. Scientific investigation has evolved very slowly during a period of rapid and revolutionary advances in knowledge and sophisticated scientific technology, and the present system is a mixture of outdated tradition and imperfectly applied 'modernisation'. Whilst the law-breaker has – because of his lack of tradition – been able to seize unconventional opportunities, the investigational machinery, by reason of its structure and administrative rigidity, has been unable to assimilate as rapidly fresh ideas and knowledge and it has been handicapped as well by lack of manpower, and by financial and legal restrictions which tend to load the dice in favour of the criminal. It is a parallel situation to that of the universities whose accommodation and funds have been outstripped by increasing entries, together with greater opportunities and demand for research.

An attempt has been made in the last chapter to outline the administrative and financial position with its complicated, rigid and overlapping organisation, and faults which are aggravated by a variety of other elements including community pride, jealousy of local government and, yet again, restriction of finance. On the other hand, although these factors play a part, the results (for example, mortuaries) would appear to be mainly due to a mixture of lethargy and a blind-eye approach. Be that as it may, it still remains a somewhat terrifying example of how attitude can perpetuate inefficiency, providing that nothing arises which can become a political issue.

After these generalisations, essential for a proper understanding of the present situation and for any suggestions as to future reorganisation, it is now possible to deal specifically with the position of forensic science and medicine and how they work in the particular sphere of investigation of homicide.

For this purpose it is essential to obtain a clear picture of the procedure at present in operation and so to describe what may be the procedure in the investigation of a death which has taken place in suspicious circumstances.

For the exercise, the starting point will be the discovery of the dead body of a woman on the floor of the sitting-room of a flat. Circumstances will decide what happens once the body is found and amongst these will be the person who first sees the body. The immediate reaction will be to raise the alarm, and it will depend upon the finder whether the police or a doctor is summoned. If the former, they will send for a doctor who will usually be a police surgeon with some medicolegal experience. His task is to establish whether the person is dead, and whether there are any suspicious circumstances. On the other hand it may be that the nearest available medical practitioner is called, and he may have no medicolegal knowledge. From sheer inexperience he may disturb vital evidence or miss suspicious signs such as haemorrhages into the skin of the face. In all cases there is a duty to preserve life so that any disturbance of the body by attempted resuscitation techniques cannot, if justified, be criticised. Unless the dead person is one of his patients, the doctor will be unable to issue a certificate and, hence, must notify the Coroner or give a death certificate of such a type that the registrar of births, deaths and marriages must inevitably notify the Coroner. That is, of course, providing he knows his job and, as things are, he is unlikely to have had proper forensic training.

In any event, if death is unexpected, the police should be informed and if there is the slightest ground for suspicion, nothing should be disturbed. Unfortunately in many cases neither observations as to time and cause of death are made, whilst cases have occurred when the police have been notified some hours later. It must also be remembered that there are two main branches of the police: those in uniform and those in the criminal investigation department. Though even in cases of suspicion the former may well be the first to arrive, it will be the latter or the Coroner's officer who will carry out the investigation. If no doctor is already present, the police may call the police surgeon. This title is an unfortunate misnomer, because it dates from the time when he was the official doctor who looked after the families of the police. Under the circumstances with which we are concerned, he is acting in the capacity of an impartial medical examiner, and will by his special knowledge and experience know that he has to confirm death and take the measures already outlined. He must also see that evidence is not lost or disturbed.

Hence, while the ambulance driver and the police are required not to disturb the body, the police surgeon (or any doctor) is the first person qualified to handle it. But pause a moment: what are his qualifications, in other words his training and knowledge, and how is the police surgeon appointed? His selection may merely be announced; in which case he will have been chosen for his reputation for keenness and willingness to assist the police. If he is appointed on application and after interview, it would seem reasonable to presume that he has special knowledge and training. But the only training, with one exception, is an instructional course of lectures given to all medical students, and he may be no better off in this respect than any other general practitioner. The only way in which he can prove his competence is by acquiring the Diploma in Medical Jurisprudence. Few think this necessary or are willing to prove that they have adequate knowledge. Otherwise, no real experience can be gained until he has become a police surgeon. Furthermore, it is unfortunate that police surgeons are so designated because, as in the case of all doctors, they must be unbiased; even more unfortunate is the tendency for doctors who give evidence for the defence to be subconsciously classified by the police as being 'against' them.

Most police surgeons are perforce self-taught and, although a small minority may have attended courses or lectures, or have taken the Diploma already mentioned, it is not uncommon for the most elementary observations to be omitted, as may be seen in the Coroner's court when a question as to time of death is asked. Most medical practitioners have to admit that no attempt has been made to find out. Further, as practical experience is a requisite qualification for candidates to sit for the Diploma, nearly everyone who is not a police surgeon is barred by the regulations from attempting it.

In obvious cases of suspicion, the police surgeon gets little encouragement to make observations, for any trace evidence such as blood splashes are usually dealt with in evidence by the forensic scientist or police 'scene of crime' officer, whilst a forensic pathologist will usually be called to examine the body after having been instructed to do so by the Coroner, under whose jurisdiction it comes. The position becomes even more complicated later, for the pathologist who is called to examine the body at the scene and to make observations does not normally collect material evidence or, if he does, hands it to the police or forensic scientist. The latter will then take it back to his own laboratory, from which a report will eventually be sent, in due course, to the officer in charge of the investigation. This procedure will apply to all such items as blood (fluid or dry), seminal stains, fibres, and clothes and any other relevant material removed at autopsy will be similarly examined. The pathologist who makes notes on the scene and directs the photographers in relation to the body is rarely asked to give evidence on such matters, since the forensic scientist will be doing the same. The result of this division is cases such as that in which a pathologist who sought to show the relationship of a cut in the shirt to a wound in the chest was reprimanded because 'shirts were a matter for the scientist'.[1] As to stains on clothing, the instructions given to doctors are to note whether it is wet or dry and leave the rest to the forensic scientist. This is somewhat unsatisfactory for it tends to prevent any intimate teamwork; in every case the laboratories of the pathologist and forensic scientist are some distance apart. That those with special experience should undertake special examinations is most desirable, but much closer liaison should at least be available.

How this situation has arisen is worth recounting. Until the establishment of the Metropolitan Police Laboratory at Hendon by Lord Trenchard in 1935,[2] trace evidence was collected by the police officer, police surgeon or pathologist (in those days limited in number) and in cases

[1] See also Judge's comments on flex in the Coventry case (page 73).

[2] C. R. M. Cuthbert, *Science and the Detection of Crime* (1958), pp. 23-7.

of importance was examined by the Home Office analyst. The first Director of the laboratory was Dr Davidson, who came from Scotland, and at Edinburgh and Glasgow there were university departments of Forensic Medicine which worked in close co-operation with the pathologists and police surgeons.[1] Until he arrived, the autopsies were carried out by a limited number of pathologists, of whom Spilsbury was one, or by general practitioners. Few of them had adequate laboratory facilities for medicolegal work. With the advent of Davidson, a pathologist with a specialised forensic science laboratory became available and he offered to carry out medicolegal autopsies. Certain coroners agreed to employ him, thereby replacing, in some cases, general practitioners, whilst in addition he also did a small amount of work previously done by the other pathologists. If he examined a criminal case, he collected his own material for examination; but an occasion arose when the autopsy was performed by another experienced pathologist and Davidson was also involved from the point of view of the trace evidence in his capacity of Director of the Forensic Science laboratory. The question therefore arose as to who should examine certain parts of the material. Davidson, as Director of the laboratory, felt that he should examine it; whilst the pathologist, who had his own facilities, claimed that, as it was collected as part of the autopsy, he should examine it. What finally decided the argument was the lack of laboratories with adequate experience to do such examinations, and all such material eventually found its way to the Police Laboratory. With the establishment of forensic science laboratories throughout the country, the practice has continued ever since, and the pathologist has been limited to purely medical material.

From an administrative point of view, the practice is correct as the Forensic Science Laboratories are paid out

[1] The latter also did the majority of routine autopsies for the Procurators Fiscal (public prosecutors in Scotland).

of public funds to do the work and it is clearly uneconomical to pay outside agencies as well. One complication which had not been visualised was that, as a result, very few workers outside the official laboratories were able to obtain adequate experience to carry out examinations on behalf of the defence and, although available, material already examined in one forensic science laboratory and taken to another might be liable to cause embarrassment if there was any disagreement. This problem has been overcome to some extent by the establishment of University Departments of Forensic Medicine.

Once any possible detachable trace evidence has been removed, plastic bags are applied to the hands and other parts to prevent contamination, and the body is removed to the mortuary for autopsy. This removal is usually carried out by an undertaker, which has certain serious disadvantages. Firstly, it introduces on to the scene of the crime persons not directly involved in the investigation and means that more than the bare minimum of people enter it. They may bring with them extraneous material. Furthermore, there is nothing to restrict those conducting the removal from divulging information to outside parties. The handling of the body by those unaccustomed to criminal investigation, but perhaps too accustomed to material of less medicolegal importance, can lead to errors in technique which would not occur if police officers conducted the removal. Then, it is the practice to remove bodies in coffin 'shells' which cannot be guaranteed free from extraneous trace evidence. The solution to the last difficulty is to some extent overcome by the provision of polythene sheets; but there is little doubt that it would be more satisfactory if the whole procedure was carried out by the police or by trained persons using specially provided containers.

On arrival at the mortuary, the procedure of unloading must be carefully supervised, again to prevent loss of trace evidence, and no interference must be allowed before examination. During the removal of the garments, each stage must be photographed, and each article of clothing packed, labelled and sealed for removal to the laboratory. Careful observations for identification must be carried out and in special cases the assistance of a skilled anatomist may be required. Radiological examination is essential in all cases involving firearm wounds or young children to establish age. At the autopsy, certain routine samples are always taken, such as hairs, nail scrapings and swabs from the orifices, all of which, again, must be carefully recorded and labelled, before being handed to the liaison officer or forensic scientist from the laboratory. The same person will later take charge of all such material and establish continuity of investigation. Other items of identity, such as rings and jewellery, are also removed. At the autopsy itself a careful note is made of external marks, injuries, and other observations relevant to the case. The autopsy is then performed, and relevant material is retained either by the liaison officer or by the pathologist for further detailed examination.

The latter part of the system outlined above applies to all cases where death has been notified to the Coroner, whether due to suspicious circumstances or arising from the normal procedure for death certification.

In all deaths before any burial can take place, a death certificate must be obtained from the doctor in attendance, stating the cause of death. If the doctor is not satisfied as to the circumstances of death, cannot state the cause, or believes it not to be natural, he may refuse to issue a certificate and refer the matter to the Coroner. If the latter considers the case requires investigation, he will order an autopsy. Although identity must be established, it will not require the elaborate measures needed for a criminal case. Whereas trace evidence will not be necessary other special examinations may be required, according to the nature of the case. The main indication that the system is not entirely satisfactory lies in the frequent discovery of unnatural causes of death amongst natural ('easy') cases which are revealed for the first time at autopsy. This gives rise to a suspicion that other deaths, not even reported to the Coroner, might prove on autopsy to arise from unnatural causes.

This problem of taking it for granted that the case is an uncomplicated one and treating it accordingly is not confined to scientists. The officer in charge of investigations is encouraged by present conditions of overwork and high pressure for results on obvious crimes to brush aside the case where suspicion seems easy to dismiss, and to mutter 'all for a quiet life' when such matters come his way. Equally, while intuition is immensely valuable to the investigating officer, he must learn to distinguish between genuine intuition and his subconscious desire to find one particular thing. The latter will lead him to mishandle perfectly satisfactory evidence in a variety of ways: the case of John Donellan cited in the introduction to this book is a classic example. The right evidence was available from eye-witnesses; but the men of science preferred to make sure and found themselves concocting false material on which to rest their case. Like the eighteenth century savants, the officer may not realise that the basis of his case is false; and as he has to preview cases far more difficult and temporarily assume the position of both judge and jury, the need for constant scrutiny and evidence from both sides is all the more essential. Indeed, cases have occurred in recent years where a man who was almost certainly guilty has been acquitted because an officer has overloaded the case against him. It must be admitted too that if the officer had had a little more freedom in interrogation, the guilty person might sometimes have been incriminated.

But rules are made to be kept and so long as the accusatorial system is the basis of English law, the scales will always be weighted at the final stage in favour of the suspect. Difficulties, however, are made to be overcome, and examination of such cases as those of Hume and Merrivale shows what can be done by an officer who is prepared to take infinite pains and be infinitely fair – a tribute which none could begrudge Deputy Commander McDougal, who was responsible for their investigations.

As an example of the type of case that is liable to mis-interpretation, let us take an accident where a driver has failed to stop. If there is any possibility that he was at fault, his failure to stop will be taken by the officer as constituting an admission of guilt, and in many cases he will be quite right. But on the other hand, there are cases where the failure to stop and other apparently guilty behaviour on the part of the driver are in fact due to other causes; he may have had another man's wife in the car without her husband's knowledge; he may have been in a hurry; and he may not even have realised that anything had happened. In the first instance, he will certainly betray symptoms of what is normally guilty behaviour and he may find himself in undeserved trouble because of it; and the same will apply to a lesser degree in the other circum-stances.

This leads us to a slight digression from our main argu-ment. A field of study in criminology which has not yet received enough attention is guilty behaviour and its cor-relative, the psychology of accused innocence. Lie detectors are still far too crude, and tend to confirm the most obvious cases, but are of little value in the marginal ones where they are really needed, and the contrast between innocence and guilt in the dock has been a subject for fiction rather than science. We have referred earlier to the popular legend that poisoners have cold eyes; and although such work must be treated with extreme caution, it has recently been suggested that, as with so many legends, there is more than a grain of truth in this, and that physical traits can betray a potential criminal. As our knowledge of general patterns of behaviour and analysis of them increases, something must surely be discovered

that will be a much surer indication of the criminal than
our present intuitive methods.

Equally, the psychology of witnesses needs urgent
analysis. It has happened in the past that a witness com-
mended for the excellence of his or her evidence by the
judge has been proved later to be an outright liar, while
the stammered and apparently self-contradictory account
of someone else has been shown as the truth. It is inevitable
in any form of trial which is conducted verbally that a
person with better presence and greater self-confidence will
be more impressive; but all too often this is not borne in
mind.

These are only further complications on the question of
difficult and simple cases; but it would seem that the
apparently difficult case, if it is solved at all, is more likely
to be solved correctly. There is yet another factor involved :
a simple case will not receive proper annotation and examination, and the vital sign that something is amiss with
the train of thought may well be overlooked by an inexperienced or preoccupied officer, while a difficult case
will be given proper study and care, with the result that
any subsequent investigator may be able to find the point
at which a wrong turning has been taken. In short, one
will be open to interpretation by others, while the other
type of case is prejudiced once and for all by a too rapid
decision by the officer directing the fieldwork, though in
most cases this decision is right.

If this is true of ordinary police work, it is doubly true
where the forensic scientist is concerned. Again, pressure
of work may preclude certain tests and examinations from
being carried out; but even the negative aspects of work on
a case should be recorded. Even without further analysis
of specimens or examination of evidence, it may still be
possible for a second opinion to be sought successfully on
the basis of proper working notes. However, there is
another serious obstacle to the evaluation of scientific
evidence both by other workers and the courts, namely

the lack of a sufficient body of norms and statistical data to which the results can be compared. In purely medical aspects, there is sufficient accumulation of undisputed fact; but in fields slightly outside this, agreed bases for comparison are often few and far between, particularly in the sphere of manufacturing technology and in statistical records. Methods of analysis on fibres, artificial materials and suchlike matters can vary according to the scientist's own particular preference, and full annotation is essential if there is to be any agreement on interpretations. Statistical records are often either inadequate in scope or the terms of reference are not sufficiently clearly expressed : such concepts as calculation of probability must inevitably come to play a part in such questions. At the moment, a scientific calculation of probability very rarely figures in a criminal trial, not because it would not be relevant, but because there is as yet no accepted standard on which to base it.

For such definitions to be achieved, the only possible authority will be a body of scientists expert in their respective disciplines, whose task must be to give at least a broad outline of the requirements that scientific evidence must meet if it is to be accepted in court. Such requirements must to some extent be open to modification by new procedures and techniques; but a first body of guiding recommendations – rather than absolute regulations – should be established as soon as possible.

In an age dominated by committees, it seems rash to suggest any proliferation; and perhaps a better title for the next proposal would be 'Special Investigation Teams'. When a problem confronts the police which by its nature requires particular attention – the spectacular, intractable, or persistent crime – it would seem likely that considerable results could stem from the adoption of a 'Mulberry Harbour' approach such as Churchill used during the war. A team of experts, both in science, applied technology and administration, would be charged with a special investigation, with the idea that a fresh approach, not necessarily from the purely detective angle, more concerned with the underlying causes and the psychology of the criminals than with clues and evidence, might yield better results. The Train Robbery case and the London nude murders, the perennial problem of bank raids, and the new phenomenon of raids on jewellers' showrooms on a large scale would be suitable subjects for such treatment.

By extension, such teams could also investigate the larger aspects of crime prevention. The study of possible crimes which do not seem to have occurred (the unarmed combat murder is an example) and the examination of international patterns which are likely to affect this country could be entrusted to such a body. It has already been suggested that English crime patterns follow those of America to some extent, in that gunmen were unknown over here until after the Chicago mobs of the 'twenties, and both the call-girl and protection rackets seem to be similar imitations. Drug trafficking has also crossed the Atlantic to the London underworld. If such trends were anticipated – and the criminal is generally much less intelligent and farseeing than the men who could be drawn on to combat him – the crime rate might begin to show an actual decline rather than a slow increase in face of intensive police efforts. International co-operation is already well advanced in the sphere of following up wanted men and general exchange of information; but on both the problems of anticipation and of establishing international norms, a great deal more could be done. Seconding of officers to forces of different nationality would be an essential first step, and would bring about a greater understanding of the differing requirements of court procedure.

The rapidity of communication which is the most valuable weapon of international detection is keeping pace with all the latest developments. Perhaps the most spectacular recent event in this field was the first arrest made by using pictures transmitted by Telstar. None the less, the

115

problems presented by the ease of movement between countries are still formidable, and unobtrusive and effective checks almost impossible to apply. The gradual extension of reciprocal extradition agreements has been a great help, but international standards of identification should be at hand to support such agreements in the field.

While any trend away from the detailed aspects of detection work is potentially dangerous, in that it encourages the application of ready-made theories instead of actual evidence, a great deal of the abstract thinking or the theory of detective work remains to be done. There is still a large no man's land between criminology and the hard facts of police investigation. Some of the thinking can only be done by men with long experience, few of whom are available. But one area where some progress should be possible fairly shortly is forensic psychiatry. This is a subject that is only just beginning to receive the attention it deserves, and before it becomes generally acceptable, a code of standards for the profession and for the courts is needed. It has taken long enough for psychology and psychiatry to win acceptance as part of recognised medicine, but the lunatic fringe still remains. In the much severer testing ground of the courts adequate authority must be given to their practitioners before they can be of real use. Perhaps the most practical application yet found is in the anticipation of crime, as with the forensic psychiatrist's forecast of a repetition of the 'Sydney Ripper' murders several months before it occurred, which resulted in measures being taken which very nearly led to the capture of the criminal.

8 The Future: Education, Training, Research

The future pattern of criminal investigation is based on the assumption that the Coroner's System, with some necessary modifications, is the most suitable for this country. It is possible that there should be some amendment towards an inquisitorial system, to balance the advantages now held by the criminal over those concerned with enforcing the Law. Under the present system, the first line of the detection of murder is suspicion and recognition of the unnatural death; and the person who is always called to any sudden or unexpected death is a medical practitioner who may be the deceased's own doctor, an emergency doctor or a police surgeon. The reason for this is that, in all cases in which the police are involved, 'life must always be pronounced extinct' before the body can be moved to a mortuary.

The justification for such a procedure may not at first be obvious, especially when it involves, as sometimes is the case, a person who has clearly been dead for several days or weeks. Nevertheless it does mean that each case *must* be seen by a doctor. It is obvious that two kinds of doctor may be involved, even if there was a medicolegal service. It may be the medical practitioner in attendance, who knows about the patient, and who must normally issue the death certificate in a 'natural death' or it may be an emergency doctor, who *cannot*. The former, if he fails to diagnose a case of poisoning in life, may issue a death certificate based on his original erroneous diagnosis. If this is not challenged by the Registrar or, in the case of cremation, scrutinised by a second doctor (C certificate) and the medical referee, the body will then be disposed of by the appropriate method – earth burial or cremation – and a crime may be missed. If the true facts or suspicions come to light later, an attempt, with the dice heavily loaded against the investigation, must be made to recover the situation, but this is impossible if cremation has taken place. The only remedy for this is proper education of the future doctor during his training as a medical student, and likewise of the embryo police surgeon. A course of instruction in forensic medicine is made obligatory by the General Medical Council in every University medical school and in the curriculum of every qualifying body. In some cases the adequacy of the student's knowledge is tested by a number of questions in the qualifying examination itself; in others, by class examinations and in yet others by no examination at all. The number of lectures also varies from as many as forty-eight hours of instruction in each course in some universities (especially in Scotland) to as few as eight hours in others. Some of the lectures are admittedly not applicable to an undergraduate and are more suited to those who might desire to specialise in the subject; but on the other hand the object of the training should be to prepare the would-be doctor for the problems which he is likely to meet in his day-to-day practice including the particular one which is the main problem of our thesis. They should therefore include how to tell whether a person is dead and how to examine a dead body, what to look for, how to certify the cause of death and what the procedure is for certification for cremation. These are not the only problems involved; it is essential to teach the correct approach, including the recognition of suspicious symptoms and signs which may mean poisoning, or those suggesting asphyxia, although this is as far as either the police surgeon and the practitioner can go. Either of them should be able to recognise suspicious circumstances before confirmation can come from the medicolegal expert, whose duties will be discussed later. The other matters which should be taught would follow after the initial suspicion and include the recognition of the causes of asphyxia and of wounds and injuries of various types, such as firearm wounds. How to examine cases of assault, including sexual assault, must also be known.

In addition, the student should acquire some knowledge of the principles of criminology, forensic psychiatry and such social medicolegal problems as addictions and cruelty to children.[1] Finally, if not already taught elsewhere, he must have some instruction on statistics and their significance.

If this basic training is properly organised with practical demonstration, every doctor who qualifies should have adequate knowledge of what to do and what not to do. Once he enters practice, he may expect to meet only a limited number of medicolegal problems; but however much he wishes to avoid them, he will inevitably meet some. Therefore, in addition to reference books – always of dubious reliability in terms of actual problems – he must be provided, as he would be in clinical cases, with available consultant facilities.

It would seem that the best person to provide such facilities would be a specially trained medical examiner (police surgeon) who would also be available to be called in by the police to examine all cases of unexpected or doubtful death, one or more such officers always being easily accessible. No such service exists today, so a new structure would be needed. In each area there should be a number of such examiners to whom reference would be made for everyday medical problems and whose assistance a general practitioner could seek in any case of death about which he had doubts as to whether he should issue a certificate. It is in just such cases that the ordinary doctor may be

[1] An increasing problem that has recently come to light is the 'Battered Child Syndrome' where apparent occasional and natural injuries are really due to outbursts on the part of the parents.

afraid of making a 'fuss' by calling in the police or the Coroner.

Clearly such an examiner would need to be specially qualified and to have more experience and training than exists at present. Post-graduate training would have to be available for him to obtain the requisite qualifications for appointment to the post of medical examiner. Not only should these special qualifications be obligatory in order to obtain the post, but it would seem necessary to demand some form of apprenticeship either as assistant to a medical examiner or as an assistant in a department of forensic medicine.

It is clear that encouraging a high standard would increase the importance of appointments, both in status and finance. It is doubtful whether the present system would offer adequate material opportunity for personnel of the required calibre, unless the scope of duties were enlarged to include other matters than the examination of drivers suspected of being impaired by alcohol and of cases of assault. Possible extensions of their rôle could include the examination and disposal of cases of alcoholism and drug addiction after arrest, duties under the Mental Health Act, and some activities in relation to cremation and industrial diseases. The adoption of part of the New York Medical Examiners' System might be a possibility, whereby the medical examiner, as part of the Coroner's staff, would visit the scene of all sudden and unexpected deaths. Such an appointment might also suggest some closer relationship between the Coroner and the cremation referee. It might well be considered unwise to divorce the medical examiner from clinical practice and hence to make his appointment, even if salaried, whole time. On the other hand, his duties in the National Health Service could be linked up with those of Industrial or Prison medical officers and with social medicine. In private practice he could give clinical reports upon industrial injuries and accidents and even in civil litigation such as divorce or personal injury. This would give an opportunity for the establishment of specialists in legal medicine as opposed to forensic pathology and the men appointed would be able to perform valuable duties, including teaching of medical students, post-graduate students, police and coroner's officers.

Whatever the duties of such an appointment, any medical practitioner who sought to hold it would clearly require special training. A course for this can be developed only in a university department of forensic medicine and would require both theoretical and practical tuition. The former would consist of a series of lectures to embrace all aspects of forensic medicine and should occupy at least six months. It could also be suitable for trainee forensic pathologists, embryo coroners, lawyers and even police officers. The course should include criminology (including both the substance and procedure of criminal law), penology, forensic psychiatry, industrial medicine, criminal investigation, and forensic science. The practical training could be by attachment to a department of forensic medicine and a form of apprenticeship as assistant to a medical examiner.

The forensic pathologist and his future

The function of the forensic pathologist at the present time is difficult to define because of confusion both in the past and present. In the past, and to a more limited extent now, there were clinical pathologists who, as their name indicates, had a knowledge not only of all the branches of pathology but also of clinical medicine. The existence of such specialists derived from the limited number of those practising pathology in the period before the second world war. They were in fact too few and too scattered to be able to perform other special autopsies for the Coroner, and even then had no special training. As a result, many autopsies were carried out by general practitioners, often police surgeons, who had little knowledge of pathology, whilst the limited number of specialists, who were still mostly self-taught, only handled special criminal cases. Some idea of the situation can be gained from the fact that Spilsbury, when he was in his prime, had only two other experts who could oppose him; of these, Dr Bronte was one, and it was not until the early 'thirties that other dedicated men of his calibre entered the field. As a result of the war and the National Health Service, the total number of pathologists has increased immeasurably, and so too have the specialist branches of the subject. The term pathologist has become a general and indefinite title; although some clinical pathologists still perform serological examinations and biochemical analyses, due to the steadily advancing standard of technical knowledge a bacteriologist or biochemist is sometimes no longer qualified to carry out an autopsy, or, for that matter, a morbid anatomist to perform a sophisticated analytical process : yet each of these specialists is still known by the generic term pathologist.

These same advances which have divided the subject into highly specialised sections make it essential that the department must be based on teamwork. This involves close integration between the pathologist, the toxicologist, the immunoserologist and their assistants in other fields, such as photographers and others. This is of course based on the assumption that future departments of forensic medicine will not be limited to the so-called forensic pathology as it is seen in the U.S.A., which has sometimes resulted in separation of pathological and police laboratories.

A comparable situation has arisen in relation to Forensic Science. The days of the general practitioner in pathology and science are ending as it becomes more and more difficult in the light of the rapid advances in science for anyone to keep technically abreast with both. The forensic pathologist (or medicolegal expert) can now do no more than have a full appreciation of the scope of any speciality other than his own *before* he qualifies as an expert. From this it follows that before he starts to practise, apart from his training in morbid anatomy he must have a basic knowledge of bacteriology, chemistry, haematology and serology. As this knowledge cannot be acquired in less than two to three years, he will have reached the position of a partly trained clinical pathologist when the time arrives for him to commence to learn the practical aspects of 'forensic pathology'. This will require a re-orientation of the approach learnt in academic morbid anatomy, a difference of outlook which is not yet fully appreciated. Unless this fact is faced up to, the common fallacy that a pathologist who can do a hospital autopsy is qualified to carry out an examination with medicolegal implications will persist. The cause of the misapprehension is once again teaching which has emphasised the sensational rather than the academic. A medicolegal post-mortem aims to establish why a person has died and the relationship of death, if any, with any previous incident, whether it be an old war wound, an accident, or an act of violence. This fact must always be present in the mind of the examiner, otherwise it may lead to injustice, both to the relatives and the public. To underline this as simply as possible, it can be safely said that it does not matter in the least from what disease a person was suffering if it had no bearing on the cause of death. Considerable experience and personal discipline are required to avoid confusing a hearsay anticipation with a visual interpretation and erroneous conclusions have been arrived at through this confusion, sometimes resulting in considerable injustice. Therefore it is obvious that the selection of persons who have to shoulder such responsibility must be based not only on their knowledge and status but on their ability to make a psychological assessment with intellectual honesty. It has been well said that it is not difficult to expose a liar in the witness box, but it is sometimes impossible to deal with one who has deluded himself into thinking that what he says is true, even when it is not so. From a practical point of view, this lack of bias is of fundamental importance in legal medicine and can be reached by the testing of an opinion in discussion before it is expressed in court. The discussion can take place amongst the members of a department and can on occasions be most educational, if somewhat conducive to humility.

A forensic pathologist, therefore, must first of all be trained in the other disciplines of pathology and also conform to the correct standard of psychological selection. He then must work in a university department whence he will obtain experience, tuition and guidance. A university department, being independent of outside pressure – financial, emotional or political – should be capable of an objective approach with free discussion of the problems between its members and hence some degree of self-scrutiny. It will also benefit by its close association with students of other disciplines whose advice should always be available, including clinicians, anatomists, dental surgeons, biochemists, physicists and even computer experts.

The whole training must be dependent upon the co-operation of the Coroner, who has complete control of the routine material. A great deal in the future will depend upon the recommendation of the Broderick Committee on Death Certification and Coroners but clearly as the matter stands at the moment no training programme can be organised unless the Coroner is prepared to accept the work of the trainee in court. Such an acceptance, is, however, not so difficult to achieve as might appear at first sight because, being a member of a university department, the head of that department must be responsible for the members of his staff. In other words, the Coroner must have confidence in the head of the department. Although the hospital pathologist doing medicolegal work in his spare time to supplement his income has been very valuable during past years when there has been a shortage of trained workers, he must give way to those who intend to make the subject their full-time study; and the Coroner must see that the efforts of the latter to secure adequate experience are not frustrated. To put the position clearly – the service should supply the men and the Coroner deal with the service rather than the individual. It must be made quite clear that many Coroners are prepared to assist in the training programme whilst, at the same time, some pathologists are not prepared to give the opportunity to train because they prefer to do all the work themselves and regard the fees derived from it as an essentially personal perquisite. Yet if those who wish to specialise in the subject are prepared to undergo training and are given a proper opportunity to do so and are offered some prospects in the future, it would not be difficult to recruit them.

The popular idea of a forensic pathologist is someone who deals with murder cases and this is a great pity because this is only a limited, albeit important, part of the work. His value in this connection is two-fold : to assist in the investigation by making his knowledge and findings available to the investigating officer, and to assist the court in arriving at a decision by proffering his evidence in an intelligible and accurate manner, free from professional jargon. Here it must be pointed out that any challenge to the evidence of the pathologist, so long as there is no expert witness for the opposing party is virtually a challenge to him personally. The other investigations which come within the scope of his work are very varied. In civil cases they will include claims for compensation arising out of accidental death in industry or as a result of car accidents, based on his autopsy findings. In criminal cases he will have to interpret and reconstruct the autopsy evidence in cases of injury, and give an opinion as to its association with the cause of death. Finally and most commonly, he will have to give evidence whereby the Coroner can arrive at a decision as to whether death was due to accident, suicide, or natural causes. Furthermore, he will examine cases which have been subjected to medical treatment, whether it be an operation or some special drug, and collect evidence as to whether a person has died of poisoning and the nature of it. It must be obvious that in the course of his work the pathologist must convey to the Coroner information as to whether an operation has been properly carried out and with the proper indications. As a corollary, he may well be asked as to whether the treatment is justifiably open to criticism. Admittedly, it is the Coroner who makes the final decision but this must depend on the findings and opinion of the pathologist. Hence it is important that the Coroner is able to assess the significance of the findings from his own knowledge otherwise he will become *entirely* dependent upon the pathologist. If this occurs, then it might be just as well to adopt the Medical Examiners system of the U.S.A. in which the pathologist replaces the Coroner. Our Coroner's System covers a much wider field than the Scottish and the Continental Inquisitorial systems, which limit the enquiries to death due to crimes of violence whilst the other matters are the concern of the medicolegal experts.

As a result of this extension of the pathologist's duties from pure pathology into clinical medicine, including the possibility of criticising his colleagues, not only a knowledge of academic pathology but also clinical experience is required if a true assessment of the ability and skill of a surgeon, anaesthetist or clinician is in question. It may be that the pathologist can shelter behind some such words as 'it is outside my experience' or 'I am not qualified to say', but this is a contradiction in terms because once he has accepted the responsibility for carrying out the autopsy, then he must be expected to give a proper opinion. Lack of such experience may lead him into grave errors such as failure to collect certain material of vital importance.

From this it must be obvious to anyone other than those who do not wish to see the truth that the forensic pathologist must have basic training in clinical medicine and keep up to date by constant contact with clinicians. This means that at some stage he must have had the opportunity of attending the modern operation; involving sophisticated techniques. Equally, he must be alert to advances in therapeutic treatment.

We return again to the advantages of a university department. Within such a department the close contact with both clinical and experimental medicine which the forensic pathologist must maintain after training can be achieved by clinical-pathological conferences and specialised joint investigations such as can be arranged with a neuropathologist.

So that there can be no debate as to the professional standing and training of the pathologist, some qualification – such as a degree or diploma – should be awarded as a means of assessing this. It might well be that all expert witnesses should be qualified themselves before giving evidence. At the same time, it is important that those who teach undergraduates should have practical experience of what they teach. It should be equally possible to arrange teaching for both police officers and lawyers for, just as it is essential for those who practise legal medicine to have proper experience, knowledge and background, it is equally important that those who have to use the information should have an appreciation of its significance.

So far, the training of medical examiners and forensic pathologists has been the centrepiece of the discussion and for these the speciality may well be a wholetime occupation. There is, however, another and equally important aspect of the problem: manpower. The best aspect of the Coroner's System in this country is the completeness of the investigation and this is based on the exclusion of deaths due to natural disease. At the same time, such a system will produce a vast amount of information which is relevant to the public, for example, the true incidence of cancer. As will be stressed later it is inconceivable that this should be wasted for lack of statistical records. If it be decided that the system proceed as at present, then it is

127

obvious that the number of skilled medicolegal pathologists is quite inadequate. Because at present there is no bridging of the gap between the trained expert in forensic medicine and the untrained pathologist, the latter is neither anxious to train nor to admit ignorance; yet he is essential if the bridging operation is to take place. There can be only one solution to this urgent problem and this must lie in establishing immediately a training programme which will fulfil short-term needs until a long-term plan for the future can take effect.

The short-term plan should be based on courses of three months for clinical pathologists to acquire basic knowledge of what to look for and how to do so. Such a period is inadequate for proper training for specialisation but would mean that a certain number of pathologists would be qualified to express an opinion and to recognise cases likely to prove difficult. At the same time it would eventually mean that those without the qualification would be gradually excluded from doing work of this type.

The long-term plan must involve the immediate establishment of a medicolegal service with consultant experts possibly based in university departments and with a planned establishment for the future to encourage entries for training.

9 The Resources of Forensic Science and their Proper Deployment

When discussing the problem of the relationship between forensic science and forensic medicine no attempt should be made to disguise the fact that team work is the essential answer to every such situation. The advances in science and medicine are so many and so rapid that the days of the man who practises in all the forensic branches of either are over, for it is difficult enough to keep up with one speciality let alone two or more. Thus to a pure scientist it must be a source of anxiety to discover that there are 'experts' who are prepared to give specialist opinions on subjects as diverse as semen, soil, shoe-prints, ballistics, pharmacology and even glass, and it is not surprising to find that those who still realise that they have much to learn about their speciality after a lifetime's work are somewhat cynical when they hear opinions based upon superficial knowledge which is either wrong or misleading.

In the past no legal aid funds were available for the services of such specialists other than on a 'kind act' basis; but it is now possible for the defence to retain the best opinion available. This, coupled with a great deal more knowledge on the part of the legal profession, may well result in the disappearance of prosecution experts who had carried out the actual investigation with no other qualifications than their general competence deriving from their background as forensic scientists, although their evidence may be on a subject far removed from that in which they are expert. In other words, the court must accept them on their individual status rather than on the basis of what they claim to know. An extreme example was when Sir Bernard Spilsbury was once called to give evidence on how much could be seen through a windscreen in the rain. At the present time, when members of the jury may be expert scientists, or have a basic scientific education (A levels), they may well reject such evidence in favour of the expertise of a man whose qualifications and background show that his life has been dedicated to the proper study of one subject. When a specialist gives an opinion outside his own sphere he may raise doubts as to the adequacy of his own knowledge as a whole and indirectly that of all experts, and hence place the whole status of scientific evidence in jeopardy as being too uncertain a means of assessment. In other words, a point has been reached whereby scientific evidence proffered to the court must either be accepted on its scientific value or utterly rejected as misleading. This means that such evidence, if proved to be incorrect in any one detail, becomes vulnerable and leads to a demand for greater scrutiny of evidence before submission. It speaks well for tolerance in the past that when examples of deviation from scientific norms have occurred, the evidence of those responsible has continued to be accepted in court.

Matters have not been helped by an insidious encroachment by members of one scientific discipline into the fields of another. This is not unique in medicine for in clinical pathology a similar situation has arisen in relation to the position of the non-medical biochemist *vis-à-vis* the clinician. The obvious solution must be that either one specialist has to qualify in the other discipline or interpret the results within his own and not the other's knowledge. This is paralleled in the U.S.A. in the practice of analytical chemistry and toxicology, and it may come as a surprise to some that a desire for team work can be misinterpreted as an intrusion by the clinician into the realms of the chemist. Blame must however be attached to the clinical pathologists for having delegated in the past work that they could have carried out themselves. The result of such processes in the U.S.A. has been that few medically qualified biochemists or microbiologists now exist, and in England that few chemists have such qualifications. Although highly skilled in technical analysis, they are in no position to interpret the results in the context of human variations both within the norm and when complicated by disease. Unfortunately, this fact is not accepted everywhere, and as a result there has grown up a pseudo-science with specialist knowledge of analytical chemistry which claims that a chemist should be entitled to interpret results of analysis and also to assume the special title of toxicologist because he deals with human material without academic knowledge of it.

What are the tangible effects of such a confusion of disciplines? The best example is the evaluation of alcohol in urine as a method of proof of impairment of driving. There were, admittedly, special reasons for choosing this method. To collect blood involves a technical assault, for which permission must be obtained from the subject to do so even from a vein, and in addition there is always the possibility of danger if anything should go wrong in the collection. A less advertised but equally practical reason is that all doctors are not necessarily dexterous in the technique of withdrawal of blood from a vein. However, this operation is not now essential, since it has been shown recently that the use of venous blood is less reliable than capillary blood (from the ear or finger). A last-ditch stand was made on the objection that there would not be sufficient volume to test; but samples of blood obtained in this way have been successfully used on the Continent and modern technical methods have overcome the problem.

But urine was meanwhile accepted as the standard fluid for the test, and it became necessary to convert the figure obtained into the amount present in the blood. This was done by a simple mathematical calculation using a factor which has now been shown to be incorrect under certain circumstances. It was then argued that this was accurate not because of the rate of excretion of alcohol from the kidneys but because the alcohol in the bladder and in the blood remained in equilibrium due to perfusion through the bladder wall. When it was shown that this perfusion did not take place, the argument was put forward that the diuretic effect of alcohol prevented the amount in the urine exceeding that in the blood. As soon as attention was drawn to the fact that the urine figure did not exactly represent the amount in the blood at the same time, a theory was put forward that even if this was true, nobody could 'hold their water' after drinking because alcohol produced a diuresis (increased flow of urine). Here science reached its pinnacle of false logic, because there is a wide personal variation, not to mention a variation between the sexes. So the final argument from these false premises was that the amount of alcohol in the urine can be converted not by flow, but by a mathematical formula, to the amount in the blood, the figure being a ratio of 1.3 to 1.

Whilst the courts were using this as a basis for conviction, a paper was published in Holland,[1] and met with general acceptance in scientific circles, showing that the ratio, *except* when urine is collected one hour after the bladder was emptied, was not 1.3 to 1, but 2 to 1, which meant that some of the conversion figures in the past, and hence evidence to the courts, were inaccurate. As a further example of the medico-scientific inco-ordination over this problem, an analytical chemist stated that any alcohol, the loss of which could not be explained, had been 'broken down' or digested by bacteria in the small intestine which is theoretically sterile under normal conditions.

Such are the facts which have been used as the cornerstone of scientific evidence in what the press would call 'drunken driving' cases. They have been presented under the umbrella of science, and yet they are far from representing the true position. On the other hand, it has

---

[1] Froentzes, W. in *Alcohol and Road Traffic Conference Proceedings 179* (BMA, London, 1962).

always been believed that the quantity of blood alcohol estimated to produce impairment was somewhat high, so the over-estimation in the urine alcohol conversion must have been offset to some extent. None the less, there is no reason why two rough guesses which happen to balance out should be used when perfectly accurate methods and data are either to hand or easily obtainable.

Unfortunately the effect of this has been to produce conflict and at times even ill-feeling between those who would have been acting in a common interest but whose disciplines 'crossed wires' – a conflict not diminished by the legal profession's approach to science. When the further division between toxicologists and analytical chemists is added to this, it is not difficult to see how conclusions which were, to say the least, curious, could lead to a popular acceptance of misconceptions, and how a limited approach and lack of intercommunication could lead to a possible and understandable miscarriage of justice.

This is however no isolated matter. An equally important test in murder trials, used for many years as an essential point of evidence, has been shown to suffer from similar muddled thinking. When no other tests were available which were specific (that is to say, reacted only on) for human blood, the extremely sensitive benzidine test was widely used, especially on very small quantities. With the advent of the Coombs-Dodd test, which also enabled the blood to be grouped with only microscopic amounts, the benzidine test was shown to be not completely chemically specific. It was then suggested that for practical purposes the test was good enough, omitting to recognise that it does not prove the blood to be human, and because of its very sensitivity is liable to pick up microscopic quantities of animal blood from other sources than bleeding.

A great deal of these difficulties lie in the lack of true co-ordination, team work and discussion owing to petty jealousy and status pride. There can be no doubt that the present organisation, consisting of numerous departments and individuals with no real physical or intellectual communication on general problems, must result in confusion. There seems to be very little reason why forensic science as applied to criminal prosecutions should always be vested in a limited number of laboratories, or why they should not employ experts from outside for special problems, as was done in a case of murder by insulin. Nor is there any reason why advice to the defence should only be available in the context required by the accusatorial system, whether from laboratories in universities, hospitals or private institutions. The lack of utilisation of experts employed in industry and research may well have contributed to a lack of 'new thinking' and adaptation of new methods, for there seems to be a self-sterilisation of some form inherent in the present structure of forensic science. The remedy, to which we shall return in the next chapter, would seem to be an environment such as can only be obtained within the precincts of a university.

10 An Overall Conception of the Future

It should be apparent by now what difficulties have stood in the way of progress in accommodation and facilities in the past, some by force of circumstance, others because of lack of sufficient courage of conviction to refuse to work under bad conditions. A similar problem may confront a young police surgeon or pathologist who is faced with a disagreement with a senior person upon whom he believes his future to depend. This is no unique situation for it occurs in all spheres of life, including the police. As history has shown, it is also not always the policy of the 'easy way' that pays and there cannot but be a feeling that if there had been, years ago, less fear of losing work and more confidence in the Coroners, a number of the problems need never have existed. It must be admitted that the Coroner himself may well have been loath to press for some improvements, dependent as he was on the local authority for increases in his salary. When considering the reasons for the almost complete absence of post-graduate training and education in forensic medicine and pathology it must be appreciated that pathology was, even at the outbreak of war, a young speciality other than in the academic field. Even so, it is difficult to understand why experts of Spilsbury's standing with a national reputation attracted no pupils on an apprentice basis, as occurred in the Scottish schools, unless underlying their authority in the witness-box was a lack of security induced by an awareness of imperfect knowledge.

There were comprehensive courses of lectures on the subject tested by a full paper in all qualifying examinations of the Universities and hence there should have been available a number of potential trainee police surgeons. This is, to some extent, the situation in the present day when there is an examination by which competence and knowledge can be tested but it attracts a surprisingly small entry each year from those who are doing the work. At the present time when the fees for Coroners' work have increased and legal aid with the assistance of the Coroners' Rules (1953) gives further opportunity, the prospects of the police surgeon have considerably improved; yet nearly all those who enter the profession will fall into the category of being self-taught. Forensic science, although of much more recent origin, has also suffered from some indication of a 'closed shop' attitude of suspicion towards those outside and a resentment of criticism. This has had two practical results in the courts. The first is that in most cases the experts in practice were called by the prosecution and, due to circumstances quite beyond their control, never had the opportunity of being asked to see the opposite view – in other words, to criticise themselves. The effect of lack of competition is to produce a state of self-assurance or complacency, which, if challenged, immediately evokes a response of antagonism rather than self-criticism. This in turn leads to a desire to avoid any loss of prestige or image rather than to consideration of the possibility of being wrong. Such a situation has undoubtedly occurred in many services where the admission of a mistake, instead of evoking appreciation of integrity, is inevitably punished, sometimes to the extent of permanent damage to a career.

Unless these underlying factors are appreciated, the opposition to any change cannot be placed in its proper perspective. In addition they are the strongest argument against compartmentation and in favour of close co-ordination and team work. At present there is an idea that the detection and prevention of crime are the prerogative of special groups. Thus, the police somewhat naturally regard themselves as the most important organisation – and quite rightly so, for that is what they are for; the psychiatrist, on the other hand, may feel that he has something to contribute as also may the prison medical officer, the scientist, the doctor, the criminologist and countless others. This is entirely correct but each must know what the other can do and also avoid, at all costs, the danger of becoming so immersed in his own sphere that he cannot use his imagination. Experience has shown, on many occasions, where two people are talking together about a problem which is outside the common experience of one of them, that person by the use of his particular discipline or way of working may see something which has escaped the other. This, in the vocabulary of sport, is 'getting stale' and whereas it can usually be cured by relaxation it can equally well, in this context, be avoided by greater breadth of contact. In discussion of a problem the attitude of those at the conference table has at least two motivations in play : how is it going to affect me? How is it going to benefit my ideals? At the same time the decision may be taken on the vote of those who cannot think other than about the present and what obstructions are likely to occur to its implementation. Fortunately, there are a few who can look at the potentialities for the future if the obstructions can be negotiated. One of the latter is Professor Radzino-wicz, in respect of the problem of detection and prevention of crime. His breadth of vision is well seen in his survey of the City of New York, and he has made suggestions with which not everybody may agree but to which every-body should pay attention. They involve a far larger conception of co-ordination than is generally realised. For this reason, before putting forward suggestions for the future, it is essential to remove the principle of compartmentation. As an example : the main object of this book is to further the investigation of crimes of violence in order that they may be detected by the police and the offender dealt with by the court. But, if looked at in a far broader context, it represents much more than that to the community. Thus, in the process of disposal by the court at the end and in

137

the crime at the beginning, motivation must play a part. This, in its turn, may be significant in anticipation of further crimes – in the investigation of future crimes, from the point of view of choice of the suspect; it may also lead into methods not only of detection on scientific grounds but on avoidance of detection by similar methods; it may result in a breakthrough on some social problem, such as the avoidance of incest by better housing or the appreciation of some psychiatric disturbances. To quote a somewhat intriguing situation which presented itself some time ago :

'A man, living with his daughter, aged 16, since his wife's death, was presented with an emergency by the birth of a baby. As he had not anticipated this, he reacted by killing it. At the autopsy, apart from it being a routine procedure, but also because of obvious possible implications, the blood group of the baby was determined. Examination of the blood of the girl's father, the girl and her "boy-friend", excluded her father as responsible, thereby avoiding the implication of incest. It also showed that her boy-friend was very probably the father. Finally it showed that the girl's father was not her father. The moral to be drawn from this is that information sought in one connection can be of value in another.'

Any planning for the future should be determined by decisions aimed not only at providing for greater efficiency in the scientific investigation of crimes of violence, but, in addition, at integrating both the machinery of this with the compilation and classification of all information derived from the cases. In other words, it must be closely co-ordinated with such disciplines as criminology, penology, sociology, law, science and medicine from the point of view of statistical and other research. So, too, these various subjects should have common contact. Although it is appreciated that there are many other significant potentialities, such as integration of laboratory services and studies of other matters in crimes of violence, to be considered, the criminal aspect alone would benefit by some common interest and discussion.

Hence any future system should attempt to create a scientific service incorporating forensic medicine, pathology and science, which should be developed for teaching, research and provision of facilities. From the laboratory and pathological aspect, this could include – or be closely associated with – other laboratory services, including those of the National Health Service and should provide independent facilities for the legal profession, the police, and the courts. From the fact that at the moment the Forensic Science Laboratories naturally find it embarrassing to examine material which has already been examined by another laboratory in their own service, it would appear to be advisable that these laboratories should be independent of any specific association and would be better under the aegis of universities. Ideally, this would mean the creation of university departments of Forensic Medicine and Forensic Science working in close association with Institutes of Criminology and to a lesser extent with other disciplines.[1] This would provide a common meeting-ground for discussion with those working in other departments and, perhaps, access on both sides to special apparatus, material and information.

If such a conception is not practicable, then, from a geographical point of view, the scientific and medical forensic laboratories and their personnel should be in close geographical association and there should be facilities for teaching, research and discussion common to both, with opportunities for conference with investigating officers.

From the point of view of crimes of violence and their detection, the Coroner's System must always play an important part, and this in turn should be closely associated with the registration of deaths and disposal by cremation. Finally, there should be established in connection with the

[1] See Appendix 2.

whole a properly organised system for collection, analysis and distribution of all information obtained.

Without reforms and reorganisation on this scale, the future of forensic science, and with it the whole apparatus for the maintenance of law and order, must be black indeed. The present structure of administration, although inherently correct, is inadequately equipped to resist the pressures which further increases in the crime rate will exert upon it. The only means of reducing criminal activity lies in the encouragement of an equally active attitude among all those concerned with the enforcement of law, which can only be done by improving conditions and removing anomalies.

APPENDIX I

A Note on the Portrait of Christie

PHILIP YOUNGMAN CARTER

The struggle to make accurate drawings of the three recent murderers discussed in this book has been considerable. In each case the material available has been trivial and sparse. In each case all existing photographs have been heavily retouched to suit the requirements of inferior and speedy newspaper reproduction and the researching artist was faced with the problem of unearthing by deduction the facts hidden beneath layers of opaque paint.

In the example of Christie almost the only records of his face are amateur snaps taken with a poor camera in a poor light and heavily worked over since by retouchers more concerned with clarity than accuracy. Thus, a man with light eyelashes, or none, may be given a totally false appearance with a single stroke of black paint, and a white blob planted in the eye provides at once the staring look beloved of the popular press. Yet without these artifices nothing but a grey mass would emerge on ordinary newsprint, so the editors responsible must be largely absolved.

The difficulty lies in the fact that the authorities make an unrelenting effort to prevent the press from presenting the features and physical characteristics of criminals, even after conviction, when the possibility of any interference with justice has been finally removed. This of course has ludicrous consequences upon occasion, for example in any case of an escaping felon where the police not infrequently publish a hastily sneaked press photograph of the wanted

141

man, rather than rely upon official records which are as outdated and as hopelessly misleading as a passport photograph.

The recording of criminals today is apparently still performed in a glaring light giving no shape to a man's face and with the aid of a camera which is at least forty years out of date. One full face view, one profile. Unless a criminal has an identifying mark such as a scar, a change of clothes and a fresh hair cut will make him reasonably secure against identification. Surely the need is for well lit professional photographs and a few feet of film showing how the subject carries himself? The two major characteristics of any human being as far as recognition goes, the walk (especially from behind) and the voice are never recorded. Yes these are impossible to disguise over a period and it goes without saying that the subject should be recorded when unaware of being observed.

This official attitude may make detection or re-capture unnecessarily difficult and increase the danger to the public in the first instance but it also denies the research worker and the psychologist information which would be of great value.

Artists have rarely been allowed to make drawings of notorious characters. There is one superb sketch of the French criminal Landru by Sir William Orpen, more revealing than a dozen photographs, but very little else of that calibre. Jack Shepherd was painted in his cell by Hogarth and Lord Lovat was sketched whilst under arrest, but he was an aristocrat paying for patriotism and not a true criminal. Portraits of pirates, if greatly born, sometimes survive but the field of criminal history has been largely denied to the artist. One good portrait of Charles Peace would surely be of more value than those of a hundred Mayors who were his contemporaries, yet only one poor photograph remains. If a criminal psychologist needs physical records of historic cases his best course is a visit to Madame Tussaud's, but for the most part these effigies

were modelled by artists labouring under the same difficulties as today. How immensely valuable would any
competent early nineteenth century artist's sketchbook be,
had he but had the run of Newgate, and what a thousand
pities it is that there is no good painting of Claude Duval
or Dick Turpin.

Dr Palmer of Rugeley only survives as an indifferent
wood engraving which is almost a caricature. Burke and
Hare are conjectural figures half invented by a hack, as
is William Corder of the Red Barn. Of George Joseph
Smith and Seddon the poisoner there are only a few rigid
and heavily retouched photographs that reveal nothing.
Yet by the very nature of his work a portrait artist lives
intimately with a man's face for at the very least a day and
he cannot fail to learn something of the subject.

In the case of Christie I would say that the man was
the nearest thing I have ever encountered to unadulterated
evil. Shorn of the veils of retouching, the face which
emerged was cold, unworried and purposeful in a vulpine
way. Two days' association with it made me almost
physically sick and the woman cleaning my studio, who
had no idea of the subject of the portrait, asked me to put
it away whilst she was working because it was frightening.
In my anxiety to be accurate and unswayed by pre-
knowledge of the subject I tried to subdue the icy lust in
the features but the revolting truth could not be concealed.
This was a man of whom one could believe anything and
his curious likeness to Adolf Eichmann will be immediately
apparent to those who consider it.

The portrait will be found opposite page 73

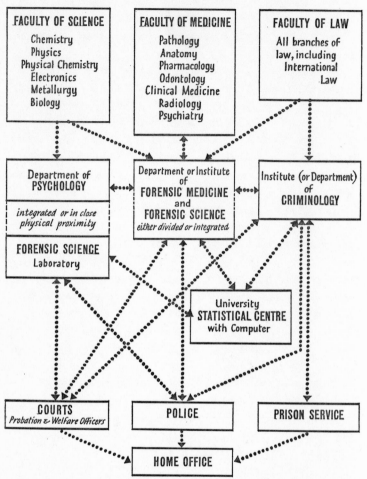

This diagram shows the possible status of a department or institute of forensic medicine within the University framework and with reference to the administration of justice. It would also draw on industrial and government research into such matters as electronics, applications of nuclear physics, metallurgy, engineering, textiles and other technical programmes.